PIPE FITTINGS

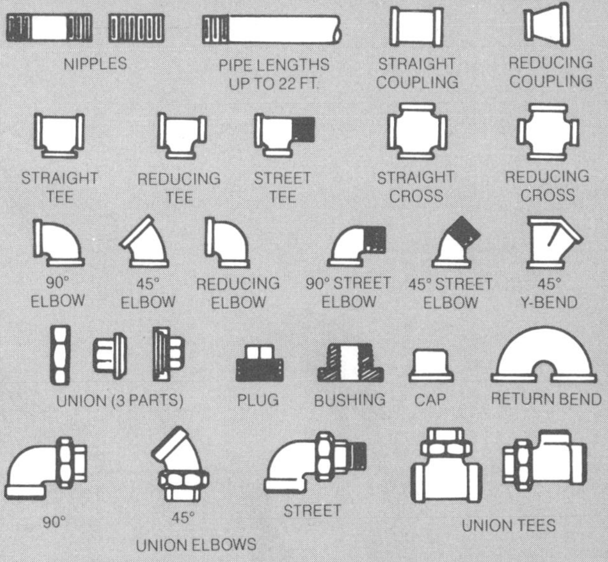

NIPPLES · PIPE LENGTHS UP TO 22 FT. · STRAIGHT COUPLING · REDUCING COUPLING

COUPLING · NUT · CAP

STRAIGHT TEE · REDUCING TEE · STREET TEE · STRAIGHT CROSS · REDUCING CROSS

90° ELBOW · 90° ELBOW

90° ELBOW · 45° ELBOW · REDUCING ELBOW · 90° STREET ELBOW · 45° STREET ELBOW · 45° Y-BEND

REDUCING TEE

REDUCER

UNION (3 PARTS) · PLUG · BUSHING · CAP · RETURN BEND

90° · 45° · STREET

UNION ELBOWS · UNION TEES

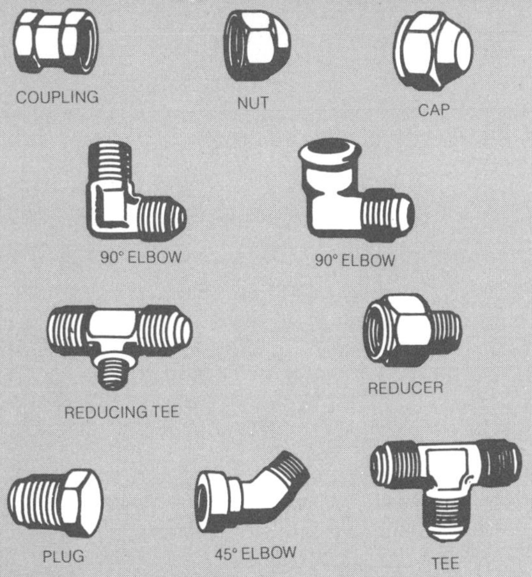

PLUG · 45° ELBOW · TEE

MEASURES OF CAPACITY

1 cup	=	8 fl oz
2 cups	=	1 pint
2 pints	=	1 quart
4 quarts	=	1 gallon
2 gallons	=	1 peck
4 pecks	=	1 bushel

STANDARD STEEL PIPE (All Dimensions in inches)

Nominal Size	Outside Diameter	Inside Diameter	Nominal Size	Outside Diameter	Inside Diameter
⅛	0.405	0.269	1	1.315	1.049
¼	0.540	0.364	1¼	1.660	1.380
⅜	0.675	0.493	1½	1.900	1.610
½	0.840	0.622	2	2.375	2.067
¾	1.050	0.824	2½	2.875	2.469

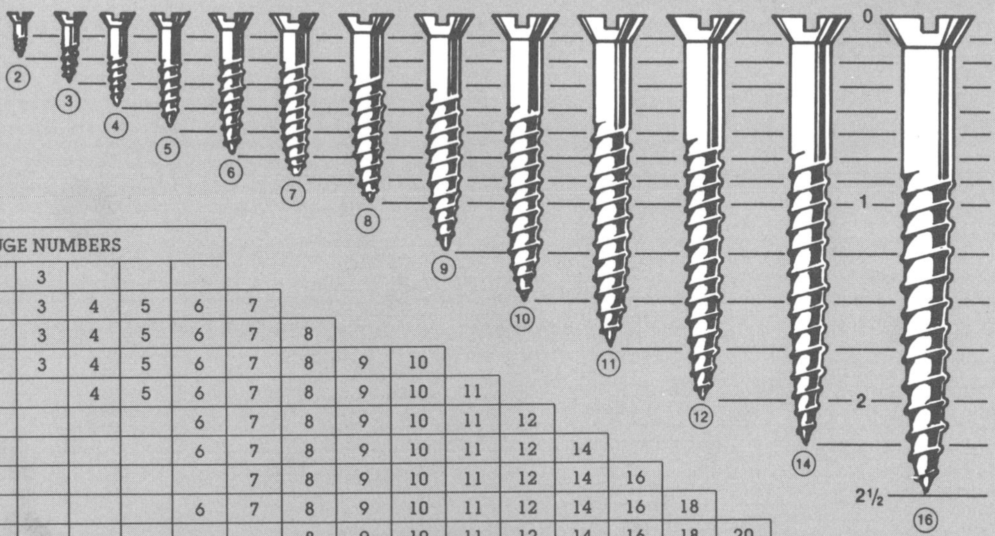

WOOD SCREWS

LENGTH	GAUGE NUMBERS														
	0	1	2	3	4	5	6	7	8	9	10	11	12	14	16	18	20	24
¼ INCH	0	1	2	3											
⅜ INCH			2	3	4	5	6	7							
½ INCH			2	3	4	5	6	7	8						
⅝ INCH				3	4	5	6	7	8	9	10				
¾ INCH					4	5	6	7	8	9	10	11			
⅞ INCH							6	7	8	9	10	11	12		
1 INCH							6	7	8	9	10	11	12	14	
1¼ INCH								7	8	9	10	11	12	14	16
1½ INCH							6	7	8	9	10	11	12	14	16	18
1¾ INCH									8	9	10	11	12	14	16	18	20
2 INCH									8	9	10	11	12	14	16	18	20
2¼ INCH										9	10	11	12	14	16	18	20
2½ INCH													12	14	16	18	20
2¾ INCH														14	16	18	20
3 INCH															16	18	20
3½ INCH																18	20	24
4 INCH																18	20	24

WHEN YOU BUY SCREWS, SPECIFY (1) LENGTH, (2) GAUGE NUMBER, (3) TYPE OF HEAD—FLAT, ROUND, OR OVAL, (4) MATERIAL—STEEL, BRASS, BRONZE, ETC., (5) FINISH—BRIGHT, STEEL BLUED, CADMIUM, NICKEL, OR CHROMIUM PLATED.

Popular Mechanics

do-it-yourself encyclopedia

The complete, illustrated home reference guide from the world's most authoritative source for today's how-to-do-it information.

Volume 8

DRILL PRESSES
to
ENERGY SAVINGS GUIDE

HEARST DIRECT BOOKS

NEW YORK

Acknowledgements

The Popular Mechanics Encyclopedia is published with the consent and cooperation of POPULAR MECHANICS Magazine.

For POPULAR MECHANICS Magazine:

Editor-in-Chief: *Joe Oldham*
Managing Editor: *Bill Hartford*
Special Features Editor: *Sheldon M. Gallager*
Automotive Editor: *Wade A. Hoyt, SAE*
Home and Shop Editor: *Steve Willson*
Electronics Editor: *Stephen A. Booth*
Boating, Outdoors and Travel Editor: *Timothy H. Cole*
Science Editor: *Dennis Eskow*

Popular Mechanics Encyclopedia

Project Director: *Boyd Griffin*
Manufacturing: *Ron Schoenfeld*
Assistant Editors: *Cynthia W. Lockhart, Peter McCann, Rosanna Petruccio*
Production Coordinator: *Peter McCann*

The staff of Popular Mechanics Encyclopedia is grateful to the following individuals and organizations:

Editor: *C. Edward Cavert*
Editor Emeritus: *Clifford B. Hicks*
Production: *Layla Productions*
Production Director: *Lori Stein*
Book Design: *The Bentwood Studio*
Art Director: *Jos. Trautwein*
Design Consultant: *Suzanne Bennett & Associates*
Illustrations: *AP Graphics, Evelyne Johnson Associates, Popular Mechanics Magazine, Vantage Art.*

Contributing Writers: Louis Alexander, *Electronic typewriters*, page 970; Manly Banister, *Drill press basics*, page 900; Walter E. Burton, *Light control for close jobs*, page 982; John Capotosto, *Tin-can reel for extension cord*, page 963; Rosario Capotosto, *You can do almost anything with a portable drill*, page 912; Richard F. Dempewolff, *Heat thieves in your home*, page 1017; Sheldon M. Gallager, *Crimp-on connectors*, page 951; Rudolf F. Graf, *Electric outlet checker*, page 981; Joseph P. Greeves, *Tell the world you're on the air*, page 983; George L. Hall, *Evolution of today's electronics*, page 964; Bill Hartford, *Tire chains—how to go in snow*, page 924; Len Hilts, *Driveway and walk repair*, page 917; D.J. Holford, *Protect your family from outdoor electrical shock*, page 960; John Ingersoll, *Bring in fresh air without losing heat*, page 1002; Ken Kaiser, *Resurface your asphalt drive*, page 920; Harold T. Kennedy, *Table lifter for your drill press*, page 904; Robert Lund, *Blizzard survival in your car*, page 926; Jeff Sandler, *Build a 'brain' to test and recharge most batteries*, page 975; Ray Shoberg, *Put a tester in your screwdriver*, page 984; Mort Schultz, *Catalytic converter and EGR system service*, page 988; Conrad M. Stowers, *Coal makes a comeback*, page 1009; George J. Whalen, *Electric outlet checker*, page 981; Harry Wicks, *Portable drill basics*, page 908, *Portable drills*, page 911, *Protect your family from outdoor electrical shock*, page 960, *Build an energy-saving house*, page 1006.

Photographic Credits: AT & T Bell Laboratories, page 968; Black & Decker, page 960 (top); Courtesy of International Business Machines Corporation (IBM), pages 970 and 972; Federal Stove is from Consolidated Dutchwest, page 1011; Pass & Seymour, Inc., page 960 (bottom).

ISBN 0-87851-161-X

Library of Congress 85-81760

10 9 8 7 6 5 4 3 2 1
PRINTED IN THE UNITED STATES OF AMERICA

Although every effort has been made to ensure the accuracy and completeness of the information in this book, Hearst Direct Books makes no guarantees, stated or implied, nor will they be liable in the event of misinterpretation or human error made by the reader, or for any typographical errors that may appear. WORK SAFELY WITH HAND TOOLS. WEAR SAFETY GOGGLES. READ MANUFACTURER'S INSTRUCTIONS AND WARNINGS FOR ALL PRODUCTS.

Contents

Drill press basics

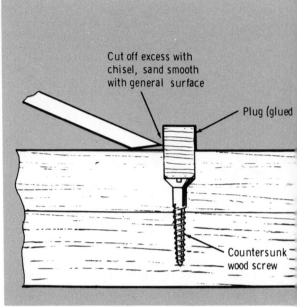

CUTTING SCREW PLUGS. A handy drill-press accessory is a plug cutter. This is a tool for making wooden plugs which are used to conceal screwheads in counterbored holes. Plugs differ from dowels in that their grain is crosswise so that they can be chiseled off flush after being glued in place. The thing to remember in using a plug cutter is to bring it down as far in the wood as it will go. This tapers the plug so it will fit the hole tightly when tapped in place. Note the direction of the grain.

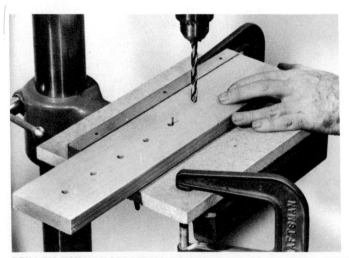

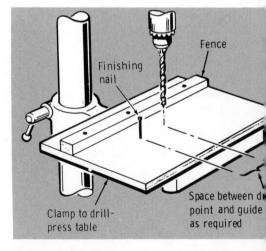

DRILLING EQUALLY SPACED HOLES. Where a row of holes must be drilled exactly the same distance apart, you can do it in jig time with an auxiliary plywood table that's clamped to the drill press and fitted with a nail-on fence. The work is placed against the fence and the first hole is drilled. Then the work is shifted and the second hole is drilled. The bit is left in the second hole so the work can't move and a finishing nail is driven in the first hole. As each new hole is drilled, the work is slipped over the nail for the next hole. The nail automatically spaces each hole identically.

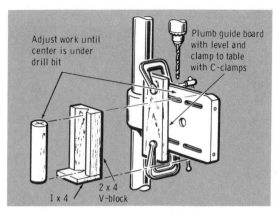

Adjust work until center is under drill bit

Plumb guide board with level and clamp to table with C-clamps

1 x 4

2 x 4 V-block

END-DRILLING DOWELS. If your drill-press table tilts, the setup at right automatically centers the work under the bit when you want to end-drill round stock. A stop nailed to the end of the V-block lets you stand the work on end to hold it securely for drilling.

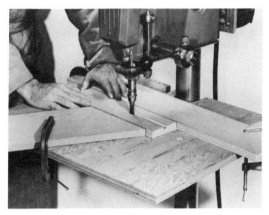

DRILL-PRESS ROUTING. With a fingerboard forcing the work snugly against a fence of an auxiliary table clamped to the drill press, open and blind grooves can be accurately made with a router bit in the chuck. Here the drill press is run at its highest speed for a smooth cut. Limit each pass to a ⅛-in. cut, feeding the work from the left side, against the direction of rotation of the cutter.

GAINING DRILLING DEPTH. When there's plenty of drill left, but you've reached the end of the quill, you can still complete the hole when there's but an inch or so to go. Simply turn off the motor, leave the bit in the hole, raise the work on a block and continue drilling.

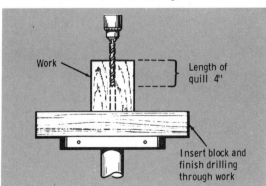

Work

Length of quill 4"

Insert block and finish drilling through work

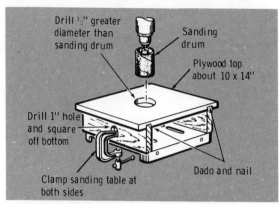

USING ALL OF A DRUM. Using a sanding drum in a drill press always means you have to clamp a board with a hole in it to the drill-press table so the drum can be lowered below the work level. However, if the board is elevated as shown, you'll be able to distribute abrasive wear evenly over the full length of the sleeve.

"SAWING" WITH A DRILL PRESS. The fastest way of cutting discs and large holes up to 8-in. in both wood and metal is with a flycutter. If you're cutting a hole, position the cutting bit to face in; if cutting a disc, turn the bit to face out. Regulate the drill speed by the size of the hole—the larger the hole, the slower the speed. Always clamp the work to be safe.

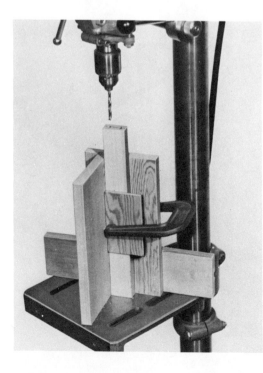

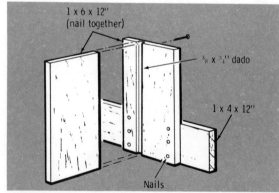

DRILLING FOR DOWELS. Holding slender work vertically for drilling dowel holes in the ends is no problem with this T-shaped jig made to stand on the drill-press table and slide along a wood clamp-on fence. Work is placed in the corner of the jig and clamped. The jig must stand perfectly plumb.

A STUNT TO REMEMBER. When drilling bar stock, you should always play it safe and clamp the metal in a vise. You'll wind up with a clean-cut hole and you won't have the problem of "grabbing" when the drill breaks through if you make it a practice to place a hardwood block under the work when clamping it in the drill-press vise, as shown at right.

MARKING THE CENTER OF RODS. A smart way of spotting the exact center of cylindrical stock is to lay the rod in a couple of V-blocks as shown in the photo. Then with the drill press turned on and the bit lowered to barely touch the metal, pass the work under the bit.

OUTBOARD DRILLING. A backing block is what you need when it comes to drilling through the side of a sheet-metal pipe, the side of a can or the face of a band. Round the top edge of a short 2x4, swing the table to one side and clamp the block to it so it's under the drill bit.

COMPOUND-ANGLE DRILLING. How do you drill two-way holes for splayed stool legs? You can't miss with the auxiliary table detailed at the right. In use, a block along the back of the work props it up 15° in one plane, while the table tilts it 15° in the other plane.

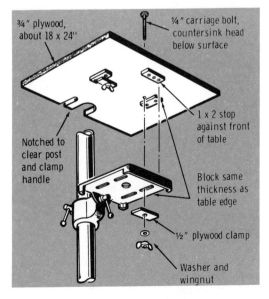

¾" plywood, about 18 x 24"

¼" carriage bolt, countersink head below surface

1 x 2 stop against front of table

Notched to clear post and clamp handle

Block same thickness as table edge

½" plywood clamp

Washer and wingnut

Table lifter for your drill press

■ ADJUSTING THE TABLE HEIGHT on your drill press can be a real test of strength. A heavy cast table can weigh a considerable amount and the awkward movement often required to lift it can cause serious back strain and in some cases even a hernia. Inertia and the sheer weight of the table (with everything that might be resting on it) can be a considerable lifting force. Add to this the friction of the table against the drill press column and the lifting force can be well over 55 lbs.

The simple lifting device described here can change all that. Whether you have to lift it once or make repeated moves, this table lifter can change those 55 lbs. to a mere 10. The cost? Probably a fraction of the cost of a doctor visit to look into that sore back!

The lifter is quite simple to construct. It consists of a lever, collar clamp and a link that connects the two. The collar clamp can be made right in your shop. A standard 2¾-in.-dia. clamp fits most drill presses.

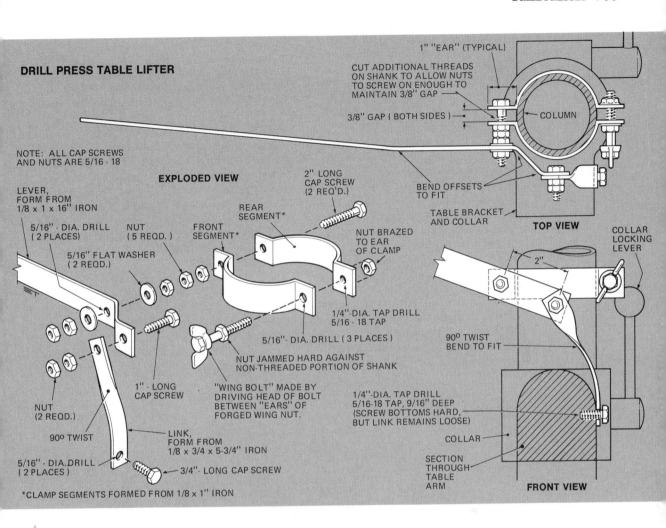

DRILL PRESS TABLE LIFTER

1" "EAR" (TYPICAL)

CUT ADDITIONAL THREADS ON SHANK TO ALLOW NUTS TO SCREW ON ENOUGH TO MAINTAIN 3/8" GAP

COLUMN

3/8" GAP (BOTH SIDES)

NOTE: ALL CAP SCREWS AND NUTS ARE 5/16 - 18

BEND OFFSETS TO FIT

EXPLODED VIEW

2" LONG CAP SCREW (2 REQ'D.)

REAR SEGMENT*

TABLE BRACKET AND COLLAR

TOP VIEW

LEVER, FORM FROM 1/8 x 1 x 16" IRON

FRONT SEGMENT*

NUT BRAZED TO EAR OF CLAMP

COLLAR LOCKING LEVER

5/16" - DIA. DRILL (2 PLACES)

NUT (5 REQD.)

2"

5/16" FLAT WASHER (2 REQD.)

1/4"-DIA. TAP DRILL 5/16 - 18 TAP

5/16". DIA. DRILL (3 PLACES)

90° TWIST BEND TO FIT

NUT JAMMED HARD AGAINST NON-THREADED PORTION OF SHANK

1" - LONG CAP SCREW

"WING BOLT" MADE BY DRIVING HEAD OF BOLT BETWEEN "EARS" OF FORGED WING NUT.

1/4"-DIA. TAP DRILL 5/16-18 TAP, 9/16" DEEP (SCREW BOTTOMS HARD, BUT LINK REMAINS LOOSE)

NUT (2 REQD.)

COLLAR

90° TWIST

LINK, FORM FROM 1/8 x 3/4 x 5-3/4" IRON

SECTION THROUGH TABLE ARM

5/16" - DIA.DRILL (2 PLACES)

3/4". LONG CAP SCREW

FRONT VIEW

*CLAMP SEGMENTS FORMED FROM 1/8 x 1" IRON

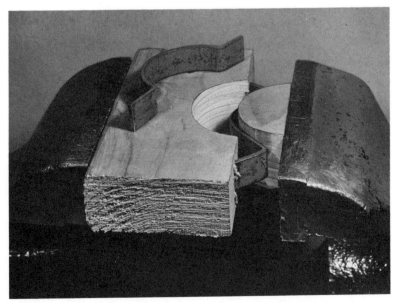

BEND YOUR own column clamp for the drill press lifter by making and using this form. It is made from a couple scraps of 2x4. A semicircular block is cut out of one piece of 2x4 and an arc cut out from the other (see text). The blanks are then placed in this form and the form placed in a vise. Applying pressure to the vise provides the bending force.

You will need two 6-in.-long blanks if you plan to make your own clamp. They should be suitable to use on a 2¾-in. column. Begin making the clamp by bending the ends of the two blanks 90° to form 1-in.-long "ears." Next, use a compass to draw an arc with a 1½-in. radius on a 6-in. length of 2x4. The centerpoint for the arc should be located ⁵⁄₁₆-in. beyond the edge of the 2x4. Carefully cut along the line of the arc with a jigsaw and remove the piece of waste stock.

You will need a second piece of 2x4 to form the male part of the bending form. In this piece, cut out a semicircular block with a 1⅜-in. radius to produce a curved tool for forcing the iron strips into the first notch. Keep the centerpoint of this arc at least ⅛ in. from the 2x4's edge.

Place the male and female mold around the blanks and put into a hefty bench vise. As you begin to apply pressure to the vise the necessary bending force will be exerted to make the clamp fit the correct shape. A column with a diameter more than 2¾ in. calls for proportionately longer blanks and a larger jig for forming clamps. Cut

the notch with a radius equal to the column radius plus ⅛ in. Make the radius of the corresponding block equal to the column's. Maintain a ⅜-in. gap between the ears of the assembled clamp to allow for final tightening.

Drilling holes for cap screws

Now, in the center of each clamp segment ear (except one), drill ⁵⁄₁₆-in. holes to accept two 2-in. long cap screws. In the remaining ear, drill and tap for a ⁵⁄₁₆-18 hole. This threaded hole goes to the right rear when the clamp is in position (see plans) and accommodates the right-hand, clamp-tightening bolt. A nut, brazed to the right-rear clamp ear may be used to reinforce or supplant the threaded hole.

Using a forged wingnut will make hand-tightening possible. To do this, slip the forged wingnut for a ⅜-in. bolt up to the head of the right-hand bolt, and drive the head tightly between the wings. Run a hex nut hard against the end of the threading. This is used to provide clearance for adjusting the wingbolt.

ALL OF THE NECESSARY parts to make the lifter are shown here before assembly.

LOCKED NUTS (two nuts jammed and tightened securely) are used at several places. They help prevent loosening at pivotal connections.

WINGBOLT DRAWS clamp segments together to keep the table from dropping when collar locking lever is loosened.

Determining fulcrum point

The fulcrum hole is located on the lever about 3 in. from the end and 2½ in. (center to center) from the connecting-link bolt hole. The lever must be made so it won't strike the drill press column. This is accomplished by forming an offset bend in the lever.

The link can be made from scrap ⅛x1-in. iron. It can alternately be made from the ⅛x¾-in. iron specified in the plans. Twist this link 90° and bend it as needed to secure it to the side of the table arm.

To attach the link to the table, it is first necessary to find the exact "balance point" on the table arm. This point is located where the effort to lift the table seems the least.

When you have located the "balance point," drill and tap for a ⁵⁄₁₆-18x⁹⁄₁₆-in. hole to receive the ¾-in.-long capscrew. Be sure the link will fit loosely on the tightened bolt.

Adding extra washers

After the lifter is all together you may discover that there is some wobble at the connections. To eliminate this you can add a few extra washers to obtain the specified gaps. We had to place one

under the head of the left-hand clamp bolt as a spacer. Its purpose there was to help produce the required ⅜-in. gap between the segment ears. If friction is a problem, you can oil movable joints and the wingbolt.

To operate the lifter, tighten the table clamp and release the collar by loosening the wingbolt. Slide the collar up the column as far as it will go, then retighten the wingbolt. Release the table clamp screw and press down on the main lever to lift the table. For a lift over 3 in., repeat this same procedure.

When it comes time to lower the table, simply follow the reverse of the raising procedure. The handle may tend to cut into your hand while you are operating the lifter. For a more comfortable grip, slip a short segment of rubber or plastic hose over the handle.

A backup safety clamp

A second column clamp, similar to the one described, installed below the drill press table, will prevent it from dropping accidently to the floor or bench. The second clamp limits the table's fall if both lifter clamp and collar lock are loosened at the same time. Even if you do not install the lifter described here, this backup safety clamp is a smart precaution.

Portable drill basics

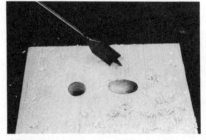

SPADE bit is perfect for drilling straight or angled holes in most woods.

BIT CASE holds 29 bits, lists sizes and decimal equivalents.

FOR EXTRA-SMALL holes, chuck a brad into drill after nipping off its head.

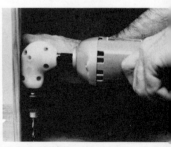

RIGHT-ANGLE attachment gets you close to a corner, also helps polishi

■ DRILL, BUFF, POLISH, sand, scrape, cut, mix, grind—you name a shop job and it's a pretty safe bet there's an accessory around that will let you handle the task with your portable drill. In fact, when you consider the tremendous variety of jobs—besides boring holes—you can do with a drill, it becomes apparent why the portable drill is the most purchased power tool.

Freeing both hands

With many accessories, you must have both hands free to handle the work while the tool does its job. Several makers offer horizontal drill stands for bench-mounting. These are a must if you want to get more use from your drill. Vertical drill stands, on the other hand, are intended to convert a portable drill into an accurate and reliable drill press at a fraction of the cost.

Accessories for drilling

Besides the high-speed twist bits that you prob-ably got with your drill when you bought it, you ought to treat yourself to a full set of power (spade) bits. The larger-diameter ones come with step-down ¼-in. shanks. Thus you can drill up to 1⅜-in. holes with a ¼-in. drill. For 1½-in.-diameter and larger holes, you will have to use a hole saw. There are two types—nonadjustable and adjustable. The adjustable type gives a choice of hole sizes, but be aware that it does not bore holes as neatly as the single-size, rigid-type hole saws do and some sanding may be necessary to clean out the hole.

Shaping with a drill

Several manufacturers now offer various accessories for shaping and milling with a drill. Of all drill accessories available, these are the least desirable. Remember that most wood shaping is best done at high speeds—30,000 rpm with a router, for example. In a drill, you will probably work with a speed somewhere around 2000 rpm.

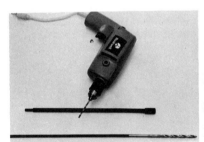

ELECTRICIAN'S 18-in. bit and 12-in. extension help deep drilling.

ADJUSTABLE hole saw cuts many sizes. Use slow speed and moderate pressure.

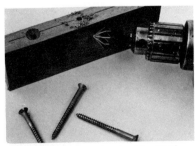

COUNTERSINK can be used in wood, plastics and composition materials.

DOWEL-PLUG cutter is best used in a drill with a maximum speed of 3000 rpm.

COMMERCIAL drill stop limits bit travel; masking tape (right) is a guide.

You pay for the difference in quality of work. The cuts will be much rougher and not as accurate.

Tools labeled rotary rasps and files work best when used in a drill mounted in a vertical drill stand. Before using any rasp, make certain you read the manufacturer's instructions carefully concerning speed and use, both for safety and better performance.

Smoothing operations

For fast, easy stock removal of rough work, you can't beat a drum rasp for curved surfaces or a metal disc rasp for flat workpieces. These tools come with many cutting edges spaced about their work surfaces; thus it's best to stop periodically and clear the tool to keep it from clogging.

Though not shown, a good sanding device is a wheel fitted with short strips of sandpaper. As the wheel revolves, the flapping strips quickly smooth round or odd-shaped workpieces.

To make your drill a screwdriver, consider buying an attachment like the one shown. But if you own a variable-speed reversible drill, you can make it a screwdriver by simply buying the driver bits.

Other accessories

DRILL MOUNTED in horizontal drill stand frees both hands to hold work for job such as polishing.

For those tough drilling chores

BITS for masonry, nonferrous metals use tungsten-carbide tips.

WITH SPECIAL bits, variable-speed drills drive screws quickly, easily.

IN VERTICAL stand, the tool becomes a drill press. Here, cup brush is chucked.

FOR MORE holding power, drill hole in mortar joint, not brick.

THIS SCREWDRIVER attachment lets single-speed drill drive screws.

ASSORTMENT OF shaped stones lets you do most grinding, finishing jobs.

TO DRILL ceramic tile use slow speed; cool bit with water.

SPECIALLY shaped bit bores chip-free holes in sheet acrylics.

FAST, complete mixing of paint is assured with powered homogenizer.

PROTECT BITS by storing them in a metal case. This one holds 23 drills.

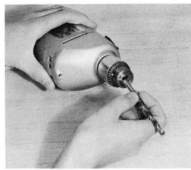

BIT IS fully inserted into Jacobs chuck, aligned so *all three jaws* hold it.

NEXT, use chuck key that comes with the tool to tighten bit securely.

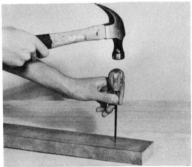

KEEP BIT from drifting as drill is started by indenting with an awl.

TO MAKE SURE drill is perpendicular to work, use square on front and side.

USE countersink when installing flat-head screws so heads will be flush.

ROSETTE SINKS are available in a variety of diameters for countersinking.

The portable drill

■ A PORTABLE electric drill is generally the first power tool a fledgling craftsman should buy. Besides boring accurate holes, a drill can be used to countersink, counterbore, sand rough surfaces smooth, stir paint—and a lot more.

The most commonly purchased drill is the ¼-incher; that is, a drill whose chuck will accept bits up to ¼ in. in diameter. But give some thought to buying a ⅜-in. drill instead. It will handle all tasks that a ¼-in. drill will while giving you greater bit, thus boring, capacity. Because of this increased capacity, the ⅜-in. drills come with motors that provide greater torque; you will find that most of them have speeds in the 300-to-1200-rpm range.

Since various types of material call for different drill speeds, take a look at the variable-speed models that most makers offer.

A desirable feature is the ability to reverse chuck rotation. A drill with this feature quickly becomes a power screwdriver when fitted with a screwdriver accessory.

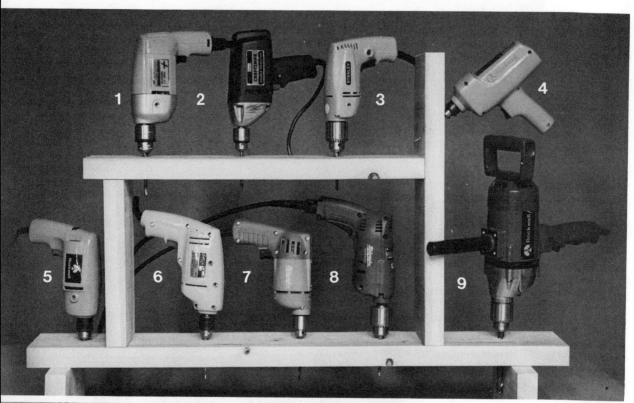

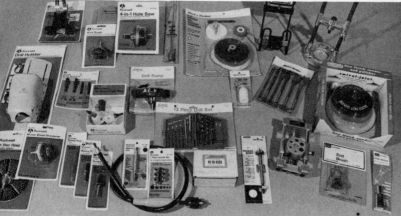

A SELECTION OF quality drills: 1—Black and Decker ½-in. Single Speed Reversible; 2—Sears ⅜-in. Variable Speed Reversible; 3—Stanley ½-in. Variable Speed Reversible; 4—Rockwell ¼-in. Cordless; 5—Rockwell ⅜-in. Variable Speed Reversible; 6—Skil ⅜-in. Variable Speed; 7—Milwaukee ¼-in. Single Speed; 8—Milwaukee ⅜-in. Variable Speed Reversible; 9—Rockwell ½-in. Single Speed Reversible.

A FEW of the vast number of accessories that make an electric drill versatile.

You can do almost anything with a portable drill

■ BECAUSE IT CAN perform so many functions, an electric hand drill is one of the most useful tools you can have in your home or shop. A power drill bores holes with ease, speed and efficiency. With accessories it does much more.

Combined with the proper attachment, a drill sands, grinds, polishes, files and shapes. It also cuts sheet metal, pumps water, mixes paints, drives nails, and turns screws and nuts.

A drill is identified by the maximum capacity of its chuck: ¼-, ⅜- and ½-in. This is the same figure as the maximum diameter of the drill bit shank that the chuck holds. Generally, the chuck capacity indicates the maximum size hole that can be bored in steel without undue strain.

There is a direct relationship between size, speed and power of a drill. As the chuck size in-

VARIABLE-SPEED triggers control rpm. Most makers offer one model with it.

REVERSING switch lets you back out screws, nuts and frees jammed bits.

SOME DRILLS have detachable cords that are stored in your tool chest.

FOUR-POSITION D-handle on heavy-duty drills gives maximum control.

SIDE HANDLE should be used on any high-torque drill.

Bits and accessories you should know about

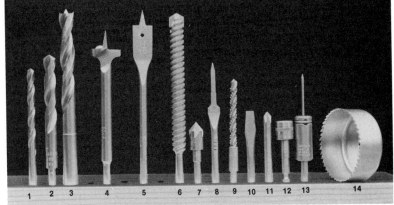

THIS LINEUP of bits and accessories is: 1—high-speed twist; 2—high-speed twist bit with reduced shank; 3—brad point spur bit; 4—flat-bottom spur; 5—spade; 6—masonry; 7—countersink; 8—wood screw pilot bit; 9—wood rasp; 10 and 11— screwdriver bits; 12—nut driver; 13— nail spinner; 14—hole saw.

FULL-CIRCLE flat bearing surface of power bore bit gives stability, and a perfect circle every time.

BORE MASONRY with heavy-duty drill, carbide bit; use water to cool bit.

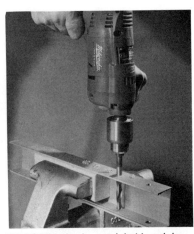

TO BORE holes in metal, hold work in vise. Grasp tool in both hands to stop whip when bit breaks through.

CUT HOLES up to 2½-in. diameter with a hole saw at slow speed.

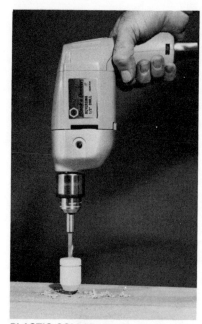

RIGHT-ANGLE drive permits boring holes in tight quarters. Auxiliary handle helps to steady the bit.

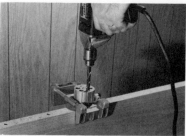

DOWELING JIG clamps on edge of board. Adjustments are locked in to assure duplication on mating piece.

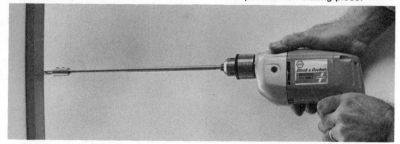

PLASTIC COLLAR tightens at any position to control depth of hole.

POWER BIT EXTENSION is handy for reaching otherwise inaccessible areas.

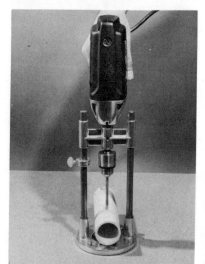

DRILL GUIDE provides automatic centering for round stock.

CORDLESS DRILL with battery is a must when outlet isn't available.

SHARPENING ATTACHMENT sharpens dull bits quickly.

DRUM SANDERS, available in several sizes, sand contours.

creases the rotation speed (rpm) decreases while torque (twisting power) increases. Therefore, a ¼-in. drill delivers more rpm and less power than a ½-in. tool. The ⅜-in. drill performs between the two—often a most desirable compromise.

Horsepower (hp) rating also relates to the workload capacity of a drill. If you plan heavy-duty drilling you would do well to invest extra dollars for a high-hp-rated tool.

DISC RASP removes rough stock, won't clog and outlasts abrasive paper.

LAWNMOWER sharpener lets you work on blade without removing it.

HORIZONTAL drill stand with adjusting clamp converts drill into bench unit.

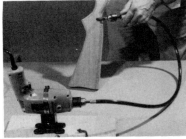

ROTARY RASP combines with flexible shaft to shape irregular surfaces.

SHEAR HEAD assembly fits ¼-in. drill to cut sheet metal.

RUGGED, twisted-end cup brush quickly removes rust, scale and carbon.

SCREWDRIVER bit in a reversible drill will drive, remove screws.

NAIL SPINNER sets finishing nails without predrilling, minimizes splits.

SWIVEL-JOINTED polishing pad and bonnet flexes to 30° angle.

DRILL PUMP drains plugged sinks. *Never use it on volatile liquids.*

Some operations such as light-duty drilling, sanding and polishing are better accomplished with drills having high rpm, in the range of 1200 to 2500. Drilling tough materials such as thick ferrous metals or masonry requires slower speeds that range between 300 to 500 rpm.

The variable-speed drill allows infinite rpm variation from 0 to maximum speed simply by a squeeze of the switch in the handle.

Practically all drills have locking buttons that lock the tool "on" for continuous use. A reversing switch is an additional feature which is handy for backing off screws.

Insulated tools protect against electrical shock while eliminating the need for grounding. A cordless electric model is particularly handy when working outdoors where electric outlets aren't available.

Letter, Fraction And Number Size Drills

Drill Size	Decimal (in.)	Drill Size	Decimal (in.)	Drill Size	Decimal (in.)	Drill Size	Decimal (in.)	Drill Size	Decimal (in.)
80	.0135	50	.0700	22	.1570	17/64	.2656	1/2	**.5000**
79	.0145	49	.0730	21	.1590	H	.2660	33/64	.5156
1/64	.0156	48	.0760	20	.1610	I	.2720	17/32	.5313
78	.0160	5/64	.0781	19	.1660	J	.2770	35/64	.5469
77	.0180	47	.0785	18	.1695	K	.2810	9/16	**.5625**
76	.0200	46	.0810	11/64	.1719	9/32	**.2812**	37/64	.5781
75	.0210	45	.0820	17	.1730	L	.2900	19/32	.5938
74	.0225	44	.0860	16	.1770	M	.2950	39/64	.6094
73	.0240	43	.0890	15	.1800	19/64	.2969	5/8	**.6250**
72	.0250	42	.0935	14	.1820	N	.3020	41/64	.6406
71	.0260	3/32	**.0938**	13	.1850	5/16	**.3125**	21/32	.6562
70	.0280	41	.0960	3/16	**.1875**	O	.3160	43/64	.6719
69	.0292	40	.0980	12	.1890	P	.3230	11/16	**.6875**
68	.0310	39	.0995	11	.1910	21/64	.3281	45/64	.7031
1/32	**.0313**	38	.1015	10	.1935	Q	.3320	23/32	.7188
67	.0320	37	.1040	9	.1960	R	.3390	47/64	.7344
66	.0330	36	.1065	8	.1990	11/32	**.3438**	3/4	**.7500**
65	.0350	7/64	.1094	7	.2010	S	.3480	49/64	.7656
64	.0360	35	.1100	13/64	.2031	T	.3580	25/32	.7812
63	.0370	34	.1110	6	.2040	23/64	.3594	51/64	.7969
62	.0380	33	.1130	5	.2055	U	.3680	13/16	**.8125**
61	.0390	32	.1160	4	.2090	3/8	**.3750**	53/64	.8281
60	.0400	31	.1200	3	.2130	V	.3770	27/32	.8438
59	.0410	1/8	**.1250**	7/32	**.2188**	W	.3860	55/64	.8594
58	.0420	30	.1285	2	.2210	25/64	.3906	7/8	**.8750**
57	.0430	29	.1360	1	.2280	X	.3970	57/64	.8906
56	.0465	28	.1405	A	.2340	Y	.4040	29/32	.9062
3/64	.0469	9/64	.1406	15/64	.2344	13/32	**.4062**	59/64	.9219
55	.0520	27	.1440	B	.2380	Z	.4130	15/16	**.9375**
54	.0550	26	.1470	C	.2420	27/64	.4219	61/64	.9531
53	.0595	25	.1495	D	.2460	7/16	**.4375**	31/32	.9688
1/16	**.0625**	24	.1520	E, 1/4	**.2500**	29/64	.4531	63/64	.9844
52	.0635	23	.1540	F	.2570	15/32	**.4688**	1	**1.000**
51	.0670	5/32	**.1562**	G	.2610	31/64	.4844		

Tap Drill Sizes

Thread	Drill	Thread	Drill	Thread	Drill
#0-80	3/64	9/16-12	31/64	1/2-14	23/32
#1-64	No. 53	9/16-18	33/64	3/4-14	59/64
#1-72	No. 53	5/8-11	17/32	1-11 1/2	1 5/32
#2-56	No. 51	5/8-18	37/64	1 1/4-11 1/2	1 1/2
#2-64	No. 50	3/4-10	21/32	1 1/2-11 1/2	1 47/64
#3-48	5/64	3/4-16	11/16	2-11 1/2	2 7/32
#3-56	No. 46	7/8-9	49/64	2 1/2-8	2 5/8
#4-40	No. 43	7/8-14	13/16	3-8	3 1/4
#4-48	No. 42	1-8	7/8	3 1/2-8	3 3/4
#5-40	No. 39	1-12	59/64	4-8	4 1/4
#5-44	No. 37	1-14	15/16	5-8	5 9/32
#6-32	No. 36	1 1/8-7	63/64	6-8	6 11/32
#6-40	No. 33	1 1/8-12	1 3/64		
#8-32	No. 29	1 1/4-7	1 7/64	**Straight Pipe**	
#8-36	No. 29	1 1/2-6	1 11/32	Thread	Drill
#10-24	No. 25	1 1/2-12	1 27/64	1/8-27	S
#10-32	No. 21	1 3/4-5	1 35/64	1/4-18	29/64
#12-24	No. 17	1 3/4-12	1 43/64	3/8-18	19/32
#12-28	No. 15	2-4 1/2	1 25/32	1/2-14	47/64
1/4-20	No. 8	2-12	1 59/64	3/4-14	15/16
1/4-28	No. 3	2 1/4-4 1/2	2 1/32	1-11 1/2	1 3/16
5/16-18	F	2 1/2-4	2 1/4	1 1/4-11 1/2	1 33/64
5/16-24	I	2 3/4-4	2 1/2	1 1/2-11 1/2	1 3/4
3/8-16	5/16	3-4	2 3/4	2-11 1/2	2 7/32
3/8-24	Q	**Taper Pipe**		2 1/2-8	2 21/32
7/16-14	U	Thread	Drill	3-8	3 9/32
7/16-20	W	1/8-27	R	3 1/2-8	3 25/32
1/2-12	27/64	1/4-18	7/16	4-8	4 9/32
1/2-13	27/64	3/8-18	37/64	5-8	5 11/32
1/2-20	29/64			6-8	6 13/32

Metric Tap Drill Sizes

Tap Size (mm)	Drill Size	Dec. Equiv.	Nearest Fraction	Tap Size (mm)	Drill Size	Dec. Equiv.	Nearest Fraction
3 × .50	No. 39	.0995	3/32	8 × 1.25	17/64	.265	17/64
3 × .60	3/32	.0937	3/32	9 × 1.00	5/16	.3125	5/16
4 × .70	No. 30	.1285	1/8	9 × 1.25	5/16	.3125	5/16
4 × .75	1/8	.125	1/8	10 × 1.25	11/32	.3437	11/32
5 × .80	No. 19	.166	11/64	10 × 1.50	R	.339	11/32
5 × .90	No. 20	.161	5/32	11 × 1.50	3/8	.375	3/8
6 × 1.00	No. 9	.196	13/64	12 × 1.50	13/32	.406	13/32
7 × 1.00	15/64	.234	15/64	12 × 1.75	13/32	.406	13/32
8 × 1.00	J	.277	9/32	1/8-28BSP	21/64	.3281	21/64

THE SURFACE of the driveway should be free of dust and dirt so the new material will adhere properly. Sweep, then wash with a hose.

SPALLED SURFACES are ugly, and once spalling has begun, rapid deterioration of the concrete takes place. New materials enable you to fix these areas.

Driveway and walk repair

■ THERE WAS A time when the only way to repair a badly cracked walk or driveway was to spend long hours with a cold chisel cutting away the sides of the cracks, and then packing the widened cracks with cement mix. These patches were not very durable, in spite of all the work put into them. When you finished, the driveway often looked like a patchwork quilt.

There are products on the market now that let you repair cracked concrete without all that chiseling and give the walk or driveway an attractive new surface that not only hides the cracks but also provides protection against salt and other chemicals that eat away at concrete surfaces.

To repair cracks, make a thick, putty-like mixture, following the directions on the packages for mixing the liquid and powder ingredients. Then for resurfacing, make a thinner mixture that you apply with a long-handled paint roller.

These products offer a beautiful solution to the old problem of spalling—when the surface of the concrete crumbles and breaks up. Spalling is often caused by using salt or other chemicals to keep the walk or driveway free of ice. Because it can be applied in coats as thin as $\frac{1}{16}$ in., the patching mix can be brushed over the entire surface, filling in the spalled areas. You end up with a smooth surface that makes your walk or driveway look brand new.

This is the latest in a line of products brought out by various manufacturers in the concrete industry aimed at solving the problem of applying thin new surfaces to existing concrete. Until these products appeared, it was difficult to pour a durable surface less than 2 in. thick. Cracks had to be chiseled open wide enough to accommodate mixes containing fairly large aggregates.

The new products, many of them latex/cement formulations, all let you lay a thin coat containing no aggregate, and to feather the edges of the patch.

How to patch cracks

If you have cracks or patches of broken concrete in a walk or driveway, the first step is to clean out all loose or cracked material. Use a hammer and cold chisel to chip away broken pieces. Sweep the crack with a stiff-bristled broom to dig out all dust and sand, since loose material will prevent proper adhesion of the patching material.

One good way to get the cracks clean is to use the high-pressure setting on your garden hose to wash them clean.

If you intend to resurface the concrete as well as patch the cracks, sweep and wash the whole

A STIFF-BRISTLED broom is the best tool to use in cleaning a concrete surface before resurfacing. Sweep away all powdered cement and dirt.

A GARDEN HOSE can be used to clean the old surface. In addition, it is used to dampen the old surface before the patching material is applied.

SWEEP AWAY any excess water after wetting down old surface, since patching and surfacing material should not be applied if there is standing water.

surface. You may have blotches of oil on the driveway; these should be removed by scrubbing them with a strong detergent-and-water mixture. The best scrubbing tool is a long-handled, stiff-bristled broom. Pour the detergent mixture on any oily patches and give it time to dissolve the oil before you begin to scrub. Finally, rinse the area thoroughly, using the garden hose.

Now mix the patching material according to the instructions on the package. Follow the manufacturer's directions carefully. Most of the new formulations dry quickly, so mix only as much as you can apply in less than 30 minutes. Stir the mixture frequently as you work.

The concrete should be damp when you apply the patching mixture. If it has dried since you washed it down, spray it again, but don't have standing water in the cracks when you finish. Sweep the excess water out if necessary. Use a trowel to pack the patching mixture into the cracks, making the surface of the crack level with the surface of the surrounding concrete. Many of these products expand slightly as they dry.

Resurfacing

Once the cracks are filled, you can resurface the entire walk or driveway immediately, or you can wait until another day if you choose. Make sure the concrete surface is damp, then mix up a thinner mixture of the material as directed.

Pour the mixture on the surface and spread it with a paint roller on a long handle. Don't attempt to roll the mixture out, as you would paint. Just spread it evenly. To make a neat job, be careful to keep the edges straight. Start at one end of the walk or driveway and work toward the other end.

Caution: Some of these patching formulations may be harmful to your skin, so wash any material off any part of the body immediately. It is also a good idea to mix the material in a well-ventilated area.

Curing

Like all concrete products, these new ones must be cured after application. They should be covered with a plastic sheet within an hour of application, and should be kept moist for about two days. In hot weather, you may have to apply a fine spray from the garden hose several times a day to keep it moist.

After two days, you can put the walk or driveway to normal use. The new surface will bond tightly to the old, will not powder or flake, and will provide good protection for the concrete under it.

A THIN MIXTURE of patching material is poured on the driveway. When mixing these products, follow the directions carefully for best results.

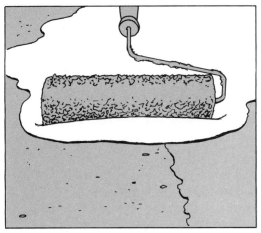

USE A ROLLER of the type used to apply paint to spread the surfacing material evenly on the surface of the driveway. Don't roll it out; just spread it.

Other uses

You can use these products to patch concrete patios and to seal cracks in basement walls and floors. They are particularly useful when you decide to lay tile on a concrete basement floor, since you can use them to level low spots in the floor and provide a smooth surface for the tile. When filling a low spot, use as much of the patching material as needed, feathering the edges of the patch smoothly into the surrounding floor area.

Note, however, that if you are laying a new walk or driveway, a good air-entrained mix of regular concrete should be used. These new patching products are not designed for pouring large concrete pads. Once you have the new pad poured and cured, you can apply a surface with these products as a protective coating to prevent spalling as a result of the action of strong chemicals and salt.

Resurface your asphalt drive

■ THE WARM MONTHS are the best time to repair and rejuvenate your asphalt driveway. As a do-it-yourself project, it is entirely practical—one that will save you money and prepare the drive for the ravages of the coming winter as well as add many useful years to its life.

The basic problems

Before getting into the actual repair of the surface, it would be well to understand the causes of the problems in the first place and what may be done to improve the situation in the future.

Basically, there are three categories of problems that lead to cracks, ruts or deep depressions, heaving and broken pavement or edge-cracking. Obviously, there is ordinary wear and tear. Asphalt tends over a period of time to dry out and lose resiliency. Refurbishing will help correct this problem to a large extent.

If the drive was improperly laid originally—for example, not a thick-enough layer of asphalt or improper crowning to provide for water runoff—the drive will develop cracks, the first step in a moisture/seepage/freezing/upheaval sequence. Also, if proper forms were not used at the edge of the drive, it is only a matter of time before edge cracking occurs. Though a little larger in scope, this can also be handled as a part of the refurbishing job.

The ground-water problem that eventually leads to asphalt driveway defects has two aspects of its own: One is rainwater that sinks into the ground along the drive and then flows under it; the other—more serious and consequently more difficult to combat—is a high water table.

In the first instance, a partial solution is to provide a shallow channel on each side to direct the runoff water down the sides of the drive. These channels need to be slightly pitched to give the water a downhill run.

Since water will follow a path of least resistance if it is not given direction, it will sink into the ground and spread under the drive.

A construction note: Since asphalt is flexible, any trough or channel that is constructed (particularly along the sides of the drive) must be held in position at the edges by a permanent form such as metal or wood impregnated with a preservative.

The water-table problem is more serious because if the ground on which the driveway was installed has an abnormally high water content, there is little that can be done to eliminate or remove the water.

Since the problem here arises when the ever-present water freezes and forces the drive to heave and crack, the solution is to give the freezing and expanding water an outlet—room to expand in a harmless manner, thereby relieving the pressure on the drive itself.

Installing a 'relief valve'

To create this "relief valve," cut a hole in the middle of the drive, using a post-hole digger. Dig down two to three feet deep, fill the bottom with loose gravel or stone and place an ordinary bell drain pipe and cover in the hole, level with the drive surface.

It is important to remember that water from below the drive is generally not the major problem. Rather it is water that has penetrated the surface of the driveway itself. The result is the same action that breaks rocks into pebbles—small amounts of water start a fine crack in the surface, then continually enlarge it until it eventually succumbs to pressure from underneath.

For this reason, you should establish a continuing maintenance program for the drive and pay particular attention to the last part of the job when a top coating is applied as the final sealer for the surface.

The importance of cleaning

Any patch, sealer or coating seals or attaches only to what it touches. If the area is dirty or if

IT'S IMPORTANT that drive be dry and clean before applying top dressing. Sweep surface with stiff broom (1). Use industrial paint roller to apply dressing (2); throw away when finished.

HOW TO FILL SMALL HOLES

1. Clean out the hole, removing any grass or weeds. Dig down to a solid base. 2. Blow clean with your vacuum cleaner. 3. Wire-brush the hole to dislodge any loose particles. 4. Fill hole with cold patch, mound slightly and tamp to compact solidly. Fill and tamp deep holes in one-inch layers. Do not try to fill them all at one time.

HOW TO PATCH 'CRATERS'

1. Use cold patch as it comes from the bag or can. Spoon it in holes or pour it over large depressions. 2. If area is deeper than 1 inch, apply and compact the patch in 1-inch-thick layers. 3. Place a board over the patch and use your car to compact it. 4. Use a lawn roller to compact sizable areas, rolling lengthwise, then crosswise.

SCRAP 2 X 4 BLOCK and sledge are used to tamp cold patch in small holes and long, wide cracks. Place block on edge (1) or use flat (2). The more the patch is compressed, the stronger will be the bond.

HOW TO FILL LARGE CRACKS
Rake cracks with a screwdriver (from left) to remove old asphalt and gravel. Wire-brush top edges to remove loose particles. Blow out cracks with shop or canister vacuum. Overfill about ⅛ inch with crack filler, using a caulking gun. Smooth
filler with trowel dipped in mineral spirits. Avoid applying filler when temperature is 40° F. or below as it may not set.

there is loose gravel or bits of loose asphalt, you
will get a less-than-strong bond. For this reason,
surface preparation is most important. Make sure
the area you are working on is as clean as possible, even if it means going over it with a shop or
household vacuum cleaner.

Hairline cracks

The first step in the repair of a hairline crack is
to make sure it *is* truly a hairline and that you
aren't looking at only the narrow top edge of a
wider, deeper wedge-shaped fault. Take a knife
or screwdriver and try to rout out the crack. If it's
nothing more than a hairline, meaning ¹⁄₁₆ inch
wide or less, it will be sealed by a well-applied
layer of top coat, the last step of the job. If the
crack is larger than ¹⁄₁₆ inch, proceed with the
next step.

Repairing larger cracks

For this type of repair, you use a rubber-ex-
tended, asphalt crack filler. The rubber allows for
flexibility and expansion after the material has
cured. The crack filler is supplied in cartridges
(like caulking compounds) and is used with an
ordinary caulking gun.

Before filling the crack, make sure the area is
clean and dry. If the crack filler will come into
contact with metal drains or metal expansion
joints, those surfaces should be wire-brushed of
rust before applying the filler.

Crack filler should not be applied below 40° F.
The material becomes highly viscous below this
temperature and, when used with a gun-type applicator, it's more difficult to work with. Because
of higher viscosity, the sealer will not fill the
cracks completely, and since frost begins to form
below 40° F., there could be a loss of adhesion
later.

Crack filler is ready to use as it comes from the
tube. Never thin it, even if it is stiff from having
been stored outdoors. Bring it inside for 24 hours

to warm it. Never apply direct heat to the cartridge with a torch or by heating in a pan of hot
water. Crack filler contains a solvent which may,
under direct heat, reach its flash point. In addition, direct heat may drive off the solvent,
thereby destroying the cartridge.

Put the nozzle as far into the crack as possible
to prevent any air entrapment and pull the gun
toward you as you squeeze. Let the filler build up
⅛ inch above the crack. After the crack is filled,
go back with a trowel or similar tool dipped in
mineral spirits (not linseed oil) and tool the surface smooth. Make sure the crack is completely
filled and sealed at the edge. You want to keep
moisture out now that the crack is clean and dry.

Crack filler will cure in about 24 hours depending on temperature and humidity. The lower
the temperature and the higher the humidity, the
longer it takes to cure.

While the filler is curing, cover it with waxed
paper to keep from tracking it into the house.
The paper is easily removed the next day and any
remaining traces will soon disappear with usage.

Larger holes and depressions

Cold-patch driveway-patching compound is
used for repairing big holes, depressions or ruts.
Because it is made for filling and covering com-
paratively large voids, cold patch is a combination of hard aggregate (gravel, pebbles) asphalt,
resins and wetting agents.

In your selection of cold patch, it is important
to know that compounds are generally available
two ways: in large 50 to 75-pound paper sacks or
in 5-gallon cans. The paper sacks are usually less
expensive, but have disadvantages. Many times
the filled sacks are shipped and stored in tiers on
pallets. This means that the lower sacks in the
stack are being progressively more compacted
than the upper ones before the material is used.
Also, material stored in sacks may have a tendency to begin to oxidize, which leads to prema-
ture setup.

Again, surface preparation is all important. The area to be patched should be dry and free of dust. Use Gibson-Homans cold patch, which can be applied on a damp, puddle-free surface so the area can be made dust-free by hosing it down.

Cold patch is ready to use as it comes from the can or sack. It can be "spooned" or "ladled" into a hole or poured into a larger depression. If the area to be patched is deeper than 1 inch, it should be patched in 1-inch layers.

After pouring and spreading the cold patch, you must compact it, which is an important step. The more the patching compound is compressed, the more tenacious it becomes and the better the bond you get.

There are several ways to compact cold patch. If the area is a narrow hole, a good compacting tool is a 2 x 4. Place it on edge or side depending on area and then put a lot of muscle into a sledge hammer. If the area is large, such as a lengthy depression, a good compacting tool is an ordinary lawn roller. Roll it back and forth several times, then at right angles and back again.

Another good method for compacting a large patch is to lay a ¾-in. board over it and roll your car wheel back and forth over it.

If the area to be patched is along the edge of your drive, use a No. 1 grade, creosote-treated wood form to contain the patch. If the form is then left in position, it will help resist "creeping" which is inherent in all asphalt. Be careful when working with creosote. It is a registered poison and should be handled with sensible caution.

The newly cold-patch area can be driven over in three to four hours—but don't let your car stand on the patched spot for at least a week. This will give the patch ample time to set. The same holds true for the top coating. Usually you will patch one weekend, top coat the next.

Top-coating the surface

Now that all the cracks, holes, ruts and depressions have been repaired, it is most important that you seal the entire drive surface with a good quality top coat or dressing. It not only will provide a moisture-tight seal and give the drive a finished look, but it will rejuvenate the dry, brittle or deteriorated asphalt, literally adding years to your driveway's life.

Basically there are two varieties of top coating available: A Gilsonite base and a tar-emulsion base. There are advantages and disadvantages to each. Of the two, tar emulsion is generally a little less expensive per gallon, but requires two coats. Gilsonite requires only one coat. On the average,

Gilsonite will cover 100 square feet per gallon, while tar emulsion covers between 60 and 75 feet per gallon.

Tar emulsion is highly resistant to gasoline, oil and similar corrosives over long periods of exposure. Gilsonite, though less resistant, will stand up well to the occasional spill or drip.

Application

Tar emulsion cannot be applied below freezing (if it freezes before it is applied, it loses its chemical qualities) and really should be applied above 45° F. Gilsonite can be applied near or above freezing. Tar emulsion requires thorough mixing before being applied; Gilsonite does not.

Tar emulsion requires about 2½ hours to dry to the touch versus about one hour for Gilsonite. The Gilsonite coating should be ready for traffic in about 12 hours (depending on temperature and humidity), while at the same temperature and humidity tar emulsion would require about 24 hours. In addition, since tar emulsion is a water-base compound, if it gets wet during the first 24 hours wait another day for it to dry completely.

Tracking

During warm weather, tar emulsion has a tendency to become tacky. If the drive serves as a home baseball court or other playing surface, the coating may be picked up on shoes and tracked into the house. Gilsonite, on the other hand, is unaffected by the hot sun and remains tack-free once it has set.

Again, surface preparation is extremely important. With the Gilsonite base, the drive must be clean and dry. A true hairline crack will be sealed with an application of Gilsonite base coating. Anything larger than a ¹⁄₁₆-inch crack should be filled with crack filler followed by a five-day wait for proper curing.

Give the drive a good sweeping followed by vacuuming. If there is oil on the drive, wash the area well with detergent. Gilsonite top coating may be applied with a large squeegee, stiff brush, broom or roller. Use a long-handled industrial paint roller.

The coating is ready to use right from the can. Dip the roller to saturate it, then spread the coating over the drive surface. Apply it liberally to make sure the surface is well covered and sealed, but at the same time use as thin a coat as possible consistent with good coverage. Be sure there are no puddles, and don't try to cover less than the recommended 100 square feet per gallon. In this case too much is worse than too little.

Tire chains— how to go in snow

■ SNOWBOUND in a toasty warm cabin . . . it's a nice fantasy. But if you've got to be into your long johns and out on your appointed rounds—which is more likely the case—you must know a few things about going in snow.

Yes, it's cold and wet, and it can stop you dead in your tracks—especially if your tracks are not in the shape of snowshoes. Dog sleds, snowmobiles, maybe skis and snowshoes will take you to town, if you've got the stamina—and/or the dogs—but if you take the family car, and the family car is not a four-wheel-drive Jeep, then you'd better own a pair of tire chains and know how to use them.

Tire chains get their wicked grip from 12 or 13 cross-chains that run across the treads (like radial plies) every several inches. The best of these cross-chains have each link reinforced with a bar or lug, and it's this type that gives the best bite of all. The lugs are what really dig into the snow and ice. On dry pavement with your chains on, it's the lugs or bars that contact the surface, and they have to wear away completely before the links of cross-chains even begin to wear. So they cost a little more than standard or twist-link types, but longer life and better bite make them worth it.

A pair of chains for the drive wheels of your car runs between $20 and $40, depending on your tire size—the larger the tire, the greater the number of links required and hence the higher the price. Slightly cheaper than steel-link chains are plastic traction treads. They're not as effective as steel, but they're lightweight, easier to handle and quieter on dry pavement. Both types eventually need repair and all manufacturers offer replacement cross-links and treads.

Starting and pulling ability

CHECKING pulling power with strain gauge in the National Safety Council (NSC) tests.

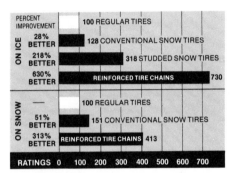

PERCENT IMPROVEMENT		
ON ICE		100 REGULAR TIRES
	28% BETTER	128 CONVENTIONAL SNOW TIRES
	218% BETTER	318 STUDDED SNOW TIRES
	630% BETTER	REINFORCED TIRE CHAINS 730
ON SNOW	—	100 REGULAR TIRES
	51% BETTER	151 CONVENTIONAL SNOW TIRES
	313% BETTER	REINFORCED TIRE CHAINS 413
RATINGS	0 100 200 300 400 500 600 700	

PULLING ABILITY of regular tires versus snow tires, studded snow tires and reinforced tire chains is compared above. The graphs, presented by the Safe Winter Driving League, were derived from tests conducted by the NSC.

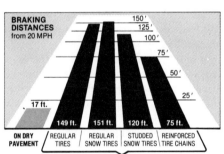

BRAKING DISTANCES from 20 MPH

150' 125' 100' 75' 50' 25'

17 ft.

ON DRY PAVEMENT	REGULAR TIRES 149 ft.	REGULAR SNOW TIRES 151 ft.	STUDDED SNOW TIRES 120 ft.	REINFORCED TIRE CHAINS 75 ft.

ON GLARE ICE AT 25°F.

ON GLARE ICE at 25° F., stopping distance of a car with reinforced tire chains is half what it would be if the car were shoed with regular snow tires. Data dramatizes the fact that in winter the way to go—and the way to stop— is with tire chains.

Putting on chains without a jack

1 **LAY OUT CHAIN** straight behind car. Cross-chain hooks should face up, and with reinforced chains, lugs also should face up.

2 **GATHER CHAINS** behind the wheel, attach end links on spring steel chain applier, and slip the applier onto the tire.

3 **DRIVE THE CAR** forward until the applier is back to its starting point; the chain will now be wrapped around the tire.

4 **REMOVE THE APPLIER;** fasten the inner lock first and then the outer lock into the proper links for a nice, snug fit.

Blizzard survival in your car

■ TUESDAY, Nov. 10, 1940. A fine fall day in the Minneapolis-St. Paul area. Temperature 60°. Jacket and sweater weather, if you were going to be outside, but not cold by Minnesota standards. Most people stayed up beyond their normal bedtime. The following day was a holiday, Armistice Day (since changed to Veterans Day) and you could sleep late Wednesday morning.

Next day, Wednesday. The temperature dropped during the night and snow was falling by the time the late sleepers rolled out. But nothing unusual. The weather is always flip-flop in Minnesota in November.

But Armistice Day, 1940, was unlike any other Nov. 11 in the recorded history of Minnesota. Old-timers who survived the brutality nature visited on Minneapolis-St. Paul that day still recall the experience with a shiver.

In a 24-hour period, the temperature plunged 60°. The light wind, light snow of the early part of the day built into a snarling, howling blizzard. The wind was so powerful a man could not stand against it. Snow piled up layer by layer—5 inches, 10 inches, 15 inches. The official measurement was 16 to 20 inches. Farm animals were frozen alive in open fields.

The human bodies were found later. Forty-nine people died in the storm, some from exposure, some from over-exertion—trying to shovel out—some in their cars.

Winter is especially tough on people who have to use their cars. By listening to weather forecasts, you can plan some nonessential driving for times when conditions are likely to be favorable. But this isn't much of a solution for drivers who have to drive five or six days a week, good weather or bad. Snowstorms in the top tier of states are difficult to predict. Freak storms can come on without warning—with no mention of the storm in the weather forecast.

You can take a lot of the risk and worry out of winter driving by equipping your car with some basic gear and knowing what to do should you become snowbound to a point where you can't move your car.

What to carry

There are two different lists of take-alongs to consider. One is a list of on-car or in-car items. The second is an emergency pack.

Most drivers living in snowbelt states already have the on-car/in-car items. These include snow tires, traction devices—chains, mats, sandbags—a good spare tire (be sure it's inflated), jack and lug wrench, jumper cables, a spray deicer for windows, a graphite spray for door locks, shovel, tow cable or chain, extra fuses and a junior toolkit—pliers, screwdriver and adjustable wrench. Spray-can chemicals are available for melting ice to give traction under the wheels. Or you can make your own. For a good "home brew," mix sand and salt or use granite poultry grit. These can be stored in milk cartons.

That's a fairly standard list of equipment for keeping a car moving under most nonemergency conditions. But what if you get caught in a blinding blizzard, snow as high as the headlights and no CB radio?

If you have a survival kit in your car, you don't do anything. You sit there until the storm stops and you can dig your way out. Or you wait for a rescue crew. If the idea of a survival kit reads like dramatic nonsense, check the newspapers this winter on the number of motorists who wind up in the hospital—or worse—as a result of being stranded.

The survival kit should contain certain basics, but beyond that you can get as elaborate as you wish. Here is the basic list suggested by the Minnesota Para-Rescue Team and the Minnesota State Automobile Assn. (AAA):

Face mask, first-aid kit, matches and candles, a small knife, safety pins, aspirin, 40 to 60 cents in dimes, compass, flashlight with spare batteries, paper towel, facial tissue or toilet paper and a supply of food. The Para-Rescue Team recommends storing the supplies in a three-pound coffee can with a plastic lid.

Take high-energy food

The food should include honey, semisweet chocolate, instant coffee or a mocha mix, raisins or other dried fruit in small packets, candy bars (heavy on the chocolate) and gum. Experts don't include it on their lists, but you can also carry a jar of peanut butter. It will keep for months without spoiling and is a rich source of protein. Another handy item is an icepick or awl. Or substitute one of those old-fashioned can openers with a point at one end and a fold-in corkscrew in the center.

Thick mittens or work gloves should be tied to the coffee can with strips of cloth—bright red or orange. If you get in trouble, you can use the strips to signal or tie them to the antenna to attract attention. You should also have a half-dozen emergency flares for signaling at night, and three or four reflectors.

Even though you are bundled up for winter driving, it's wise to pack extra clothing. Take along high boots or snowmobile boots, a stocking cap or winter hat with ear flaps and a padded jacket or heavy coat. The jacket or coat can be a castoff you happen to have around the house.

That's the basic list. If you want to go first

Useful items to be carried at all times

First-aid kit, $2.50—$6
Flares (set of three), $1.75 set
Tire inflator, $1 each
Flashlight (magnetic), $2 each
Tire pressure gauge, $1.50—$5
Fire extinguisher (1 lb.), *$3.75 each
Jumper cables, *$7.95 pair
Blanket, $5—$8
Graphite aerosol spray, 75 cents each
Wiping cloth, 50 cents each
Chock blocks, $2 pr.
Warning triangle, *$7.49 each
Pencil and notebook, 50 cents each
*AAA price or est. retail price

Specific items to be carried in winter

Small snow shovel, *$2.35 each
Ice scraper—snow brush, $1.50 each
Reinforced tire chains, $20 set
Traction mats, *$1.95 pr.
*Items available through American Automobile Assn. (AAA).

---

class, add a thermal or space blanket, sleeping bag, thermal underwear, a hand-heating gadget, transistor radio (so you don't drain the battery playing the car radio), snowshoes and all the fancy stuff sold for snowmobilers and skiers.

First rule: don't panic

Now that you have all the gear, what do you do if you get zonked a hundred miles from nowhere?

The first rule, according to veterans of Minnesota winters, is don't panic. The storm will end eventually.

Stay in or near the car. You can leave it to find help if you know exactly where you are or you can see lights or human activity within walking distance. But if you don't know the territory, it's better to stay with the car. Even if you know where you are, don't try to walk for help until the storm lets up.

Don't attempt to push or shovel the car out of a heavy drift by yourself. You can try digging out if you have three or four people with you to share the shoveling.

If you shovel or exert yourself in any way that causes you to perspire, ventilate your clothes. Wet clothes lose insulation.

Keep front windows cracked an inch or so to let fresh air enter the car at all times. A freezing or wind-driven snow that drifts can seal a car so tight you can't get oxygen.

Don't sack out for any length of time. It's all right to doze, but it's important to exercise to keep warm. Move around in the car, climb from front seat to back, shake your arms and legs, clap your hands—anything to keep up your circulation. If there are others in the car, take turns sleeping. Someone should be on watch to signal for help if a rescue crew shows up.

Keep a light on

Turn on the dome light of the car at night and leave it on. Road crews and snowmobile rescue units can see a small light from a long distance. You can turn on the engine to run the heater and play the radio at times, providing you are certain no exhaust is seeping into the car.

How long will you have to wait to be rescued? That depends on the intensity of the storm, how long it lasts and how many other motorists are in the same fix. Rescue crews in the Midwest usually get to snowbound cars on heavily traveled roads within 24 to 36 hours. If you are in an isolated area, you might have to wait three or four days.

Used car buying tips

■ NEW CARS COST too much, and so do used lemons. So the trick is to find a used car that's as good as new and a few thousand dollars less expensive. Impossible? Not if you can remove the gamble. And you *can*.

When you begin those treks down used-car row, your best friend is patience. So often people rush into a used-car deal as if there's no tomorrow. Salesmen capitalize on buyer impatience. "Better hurry and decide now," the salesman may tell you, "because there's another customer itching to buy this car." Never let that sort of talk stampede you. If it takes you two weeks to find just the right car—even two months—don't rush yourself.

1. While you're settling down, think long and hard about what sort of car you really need. Everyone's talking small cars these days. But if you've got five kids, two dogs, a 15-foot house trailer and you're a rock hound, it's not likely you'll be totally happy with a used subcompact as your family car.

Common sense tells you to balance such factors as passenger and carrying capacity, fuel economy, number of doors and so forth against the size of your family (present and future), how long you plan to keep the car, plus cost and availability of repairs.

Make and year of car aren't as important as condition and the candidate's ability to fill your needs. Say you've settled on a particular Dart as your ideal year, size and type of car. Don't look just at that Dart, though. Look too at same-age

Novas, Mavericks, Valiants, Hornets, Comets, Apollos, Omegas, Venturas, Volvos and Peugeots. That way you open up a lot more prospects for finding a good, clean low-mileage used compact.

2. Eyeball the car. Check for exterior ripples and defects by sighting down all sheet-metal surfaces: fenders, hood, decklid, doors, roof. Ripples mean bodywork, possibly because of an accident or rust holes. Fresh paint and/or paint over-spray might mean the same thing. Remember that light colors tend to hide ripples and blemishes. Always inspect a used car in sunlight, never at dusk (after working hours) or under artificial lamps of any type.

3. Also look for interior abuse. The odometer reading should match pedal and carpet wear and seat sag. Be on the lookout for a punctured headliner, ripped seats, scorched fabric, a scuffed package tray, re-dyed carpets or vinyl, new rugs and new pedal pads.

Most used cars have been "detailed," which means the dealer, or a shop that works for him, has tried to cover signs of wear and tear with dye jobs, a new package tray, new trunk mat, respraying the dashboard padding, spraying carpets or replacing worn ones, installing new armrests, even reglazing bull's-eyes in windshields. Be alert for "detail" jobs and try to look beyond them.

4. Detailing extends to the used car's mechanicals. Detailers usually steam-clean and then spray-paint the engine, radiator, air-cleaner and the like, and sometimes they replace underhood decals. The purpose again is to make the car look as new as possible, and that's fine, but it masks

evidence of the car's previous use and maintenance. A gummy, grease-encrusted engine at least tells you something about the car's history. A detailed engine tells you nothing. Again, you have to look beyond the fresh paint and new decals. Search for areas that have eluded the detailer. Check, for example, the condition of the battery box, fan belts, air-cleaner element, cracked ignition wires, rusty sparkplugs and so forth.

Smoke from the oil filler or breather, especially if it's heavy, can tell you that the running engine is burning or pumping oil. Rusty water spots on the cowl give clues to previous radiator boilovers.

5. Make sure everything works. Prospective buyers always try a car's radio (and dealers therefore make sure it's playing), but also note whether gauges are functioning. Roll all windows up and down. Test lights, locks, air-conditioner, heater, all accessories, seat adjustment.

6. The biggest gamble remover, the best warranty, the greatest lemon protection you can give yourself when you're shopping for a used car is this step: Take every car you're seriously considering buying to a professional mechanic or an auto diagnostic clinic for a thorough check. Such an inspection usually costs only a few dollars. Make an appointment with the shop or person who'll do the inspecting, then drive the candidate car to that place of business. Tell the used-car dealer that you'll be doing this, and if he won't let you (he'll say his insurance doesn't cover such events, but that's not so), forget that car.

7. Brakes and front-end alignment. The mechanic should pull one front wheel or drum to inspect the disc or lining. At the same time he should test the front end for play in the ball joints, steering, links, and suspension components. Front-end maladies can be particularly expensive, and most used-car buyers never test for them before they make their purchase.

8. While the car is still on the lift, have the mechanic look for frame damage or bent underpinnings that might indicate past collisions. Also poke around for rust holes, not just in the rockers and floor pan but also in the exhaust system-muffler, pipes, catalytic converter, and so forth. Note condition of all four tires plus springs and especially shocks. And look for telltale leaks from brake cylinders and lines, engine, transmission, rear axle, radiator and gas tank. Any abnormal leaks (a *little* lube leakage is normal) could spell bills soon.

9. After the diagnostician gets the car back on the ground, let him take it for a short test drive. Ask to have the transmission operation checked, noting smoothness of shifting, delay in going into gear, and play in universal joints and rear axle.

At some point he should also remove the transmission dipstick and sniff the fluid for the odor of scorching. That simple test can often tell volumes about an automatic transmission's condition.

In cars with manual gearboxes, clutch action should be smooth and positive. Shifts shouldn't demand struggle or guesswork. If the stick ever pops out of gear during acceleration or deceleration, or if you hear growling or rapping sounds from the transmission, be wary.

10. During a test drive, even if it's only to the shop making your professional inspection, listen for odd noises, rattles and hums. Mention these to the mechanic. Also check brakes for veer, steering for play, suspension for bounciness or looseness. Accelerate and decelerate sharply to conduct your own test for sloppy U-joints and rear axle.

11. Try to avoid cars with four-barrel carburetors. Four barrels almost always take premium fuel. Engines with two-barrel and single-barrel carbs get by on regular gas. It's not the four-barrel carb that makes a car burn premium—it's the higher compression ratio and advanced ignition timing that go along with four-barrels.

12. The Federal Government is now trying to do something about the verbal promises and false claims some used car dealers have made, never intending to honor. The Federal Trade Commission (FTC) now has a rule that requires the dealer to tell you, through a Buyers-Guide window sticker, about any warranty coverage, including how long the coverage lasts and what part of the total repair costs the dealer will pay.

This window sticker will also contain a list of 14 major systems of an automobile and a reminder to you about some of the things that can go wrong in a car in each of these systems. The FTC rule encourages you as a used-car customer to ask the dealer if you can have a prepurchase inspection and warns against relying on spoken promises that are not confirmed in writing.

Consumer groups wanted the FTC to require dealers to post any problems in those systems that the dealer was aware of. This would have given the buyer some idea of the car's condition. This provision is not in the FTC ruling, so you'll have to check for yourself what defects, if any, you can find, using the window sticker checklist as a guide.

13. When you buy a used car, try to avoid financing if you possibly can. Pay cash instead. You nearly always up the cost of a used car by a third or so through financing and mandatory insurance.

14. If you must finance, shop for terms as you shop for the car. Life insurance and credit union loans are least expensive; dealer and finance-company loans are most expensive, with banks in the middle. Pay off a loan as quickly as possible.

And set a ceiling on what you plan to pay for a car.

15. You've probably asked yourself whether you should buy from a private party, a used-car dealer, or a new-car dealer who carries used cars. All three have good and bad points, but experts pretty much agree that you get the best cars from small, clean, neat, independent used-car lots. These dealers often buy the creampuffs of new-car trade-ins. Try to deal with the lot owner directly, not one of his commissioned salesmen.

Buying from a private party can lead to heartaches, especially if something goes grossly wrong with the car or deal. Buying from a new-car dealer usually means paying more than at an independent lot, because the new-car dealer has greater overhead —but you'll usually get some type of warranty on the car, usually 60 to 90 days. These, though, are generalities and don't apply in every situation. You probably ought to shop all three before you decide.

16. Don't be afraid to dicker, but never get huffy or nasty during price negotiations. Again, be patient—use time to your advantage. Never panic when the salesman urges you to buy today. Prices don't change or cars vanish that quickly.

17. Avoid trading in your present car if possible. Sell your old car privately before you buy a newer one. Be shopping, though, while you're selling your present car. If you can sell it privately, you'll be more likely to get "retail" for it. As a trade-in, though, you'll never get more than "wholesale." Also, the cash from a private sale will give you a price and financing advantage.

18. Where do you find out what used cars are worth? Banks and finance companies can and will lend you used-car price guides—so-called "blue books." These are much more accurate than the ones you can buy on newsstands. Ask one of the bank loan officers to lend you a blue book. Figures shown will let you check asking prices of cars for sale and will also let you put a realistic value on your present car when selling or trading it.

19. Put no faith in used-car warranties of any sort. They might or might not prove worth the paper they're written on. Never let a warranty sway you toward a purchase. A used-car dealer's reputation counts for a lot more than any warranty. Remember that you never get any sort of warranty from a private seller; also that your best warranty is the used-car inspection mentioned in No. 6.

20. Sign nothing—no sale contract, no power of attorney, no credit application—until you've read it completely and understood every word. Now that's easy to say and hard to do. If you have questions, let the salesman explain. And if his explanations don't make sense, take a copy of the document to your attorney for interpretation.

All blanks in a contract should be filled in before you sign it. Leave no deposits while test driving a car or having it inspected. Do not let the dealer "park" or drive your car for you if you're not planning to trade it in. Your car might end up being a "hostage" while the dealer wears your patience and resistance by keeping you waiting.

The best used cars are usually from two to four years old, with between 10,000 and 15,000 miles a year on the odometer. The average American car, properly treated and maintained, will give 100,000 miles of service before a major mechanical breakdown. Body longevity varies with locality and depends largely on salt corrosion.

If you keep these 20 points in mind, your chances of finding a good, reliable, trouble-free used car are around 80 percent. Which means there's still a risk. But then there's a risk in buying a new car, too, and considering how much less used cars cost than new ones, their risk factor at 80 percent still makes them more attractive.

Drywall hole patching

■ THE USUAL WAY to repair a hole in drywall involves enlarging the hole by cutting it back to the centers of the closest studs. Then a large patch is nailed to the studs and the joints are concealed with tape.

Using the method shown, however, you can repair the same hole (in a wall or other *vertical* surface) simply and quickly with a smaller plasterboard patch. Doing it this way eliminates the joint tape step.

1 This doorknob-size hole is a disturbing but common sight in drywall houses where children and teenagers live.

2 Use a keyhole or sabre saw to cut damaged area into a square or rectangle. Watch for pipes or wires behind wall.

3 Cut a plasterboard patch 2 in. large than the hole on each side. Centered the back of the patch, mark an area in. smaller than the hole on each side Score the lines with a knife; cut throu the paper and *slightly* into the plaster

4 Snap and peel paper backing and plaster from borders. Leave center plaster attached to front border paper.

5 Sand only the outer edges of the paper with 120-grit abrasive until they taper as much as possible. This will assure invisible joints.

6 Apply joint compound to the back the patch. Make sure you put a heav deposit around inside corners.

7 Position the patch, then carefully press it into the damaged area.

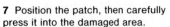

8 Using a 4-in.-wide, flexible drywall knife, go over the patch and squeeze its paper edges flush with the wall. Be sure to work over the entire surface of the joint, so the compound around the patch will adhere properly to the wall.

9 Let the initial coat dry 24 hours. Sand smooth. Apply a thin coat. Whe dry, sand this coat, paying attention the edges. Prime and paint.

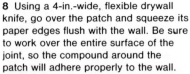

Plasterboard techniques

■ GYPSUM-CORE plasterboard provides a low-cost interior-finish wall that is an ideal surface for both paint and wall coverings. When it is installed properly, your walls can have the smooth look of plaster. Plasterboard is available in fire-resistant grades that meet most building codes too. Most codes require this type on walls between house and attached garage.

Many of the techniques for repair of plaster-board surfaces are the same as for new installation, and professionals frequently use plasterboard to replace large areas of damaged plaster.

When joints, nailheads and corners in an installation are finished, allowed to dry thoroughly and sanded, the entire surface should receive a coat of vinyl or oil-base primer-sealer to assure uniform absorption of paint or wall-covering adhesive.

NAILS

Wallboard thickness	Nail type	Per 1000 sq. ft. of wallboard
⅜", ½"	1¼" annular-threaded wallboard nail	6 lbs.
⅝"	1⅜" annular-threaded wallboard nail	6 lbs.

Estimating materials

Start by making a drawing of the surfaces to be covered with plasterboard and planning the arrangement of panels. Use the longest panels you can to reduce the number of end joints. Horizontal application to a wall is often preferred for this reason. Vertical application is desirable where the ceiling height of a wall is more than 8 ft. 2 in. or the wall space to be surfaced is 4 ft. wide or narrower. Where end joints cannot be avoided, they should be staggered.

The installation method that uses both an adhesive and nails is not only quicker, because there are fewer nails to

PREMIXED JOINT COMPOUND AND TAPE

Plasterboard (sq. ft.)	Ready-mix joint compound (gals.)	Wallboard tape (rolls)
100-200	1	2/60'
300-400	2	3/60'
500-600	3	1/250'
700-800	4	1/250', 1/60'
900-1000	5	1/250', 2/60'

drive and conceal, but also means a better-quality installation than nails alone. With this method, you will require about half as many nails as indicated in the chart at left above; for a professional-grade installation, you will need a quart tube of adhesive for every two 4x8 panels (64 sq. ft.).

Use the chart above to estimate the quantities of wallboard tape and ready-mix joint compound (spackling compound) you will need. Joint compound is also available in dry powder form; allow 60 lbs. per 1000 sq. ft. of surface.

Tools required

1. Wallboard cutting knife or utility knife
2. Wallboard hammer or crown-head claw hammer
3. 4-ft. T-square or steel straightedge
4. Steel tape measure
5. Keyhole saw or sabre saw
6. Joint-finishing knives, 4- and 10-in. blades
7. Pan for joint compound (mortarboard)
8. Medium-grade sandpaper and block
9. Cartridge-type caulking gun (for adhesive)
10. Corner-taping tool (optional)

Cutting plasterboard

Using a T-square to get an aligned straightedge, hold a wallboard or utility knife perpendicular to the surface and score completely through the face paper. The board can then be snapped with a firm, even pressure. Folding back the snapped-off section, cut through back paper with the knife. Use sandpaper to smooth any rough edges. Use a keyhole saw or sabre saw to cut any needed openings in panel; be sure to measure them carefully.

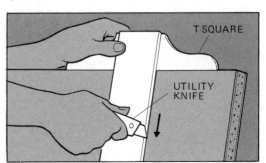

T-SQUARE

UTILITY KNIFE

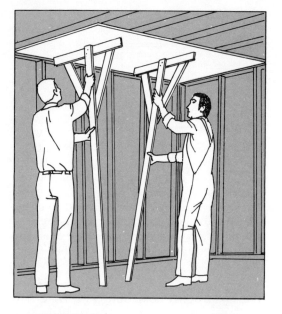

Ceiling installation

Ceilings should be covered before walls. Panels are held in place for nailing with support tees; make them about 1 in. longer than floor-to-ceiling height. Place nails 7 in. apart. If the adhesive-and-nails method is used, all edges should still be nailed, but only one nail per ceiling joist will be required in the "field" of the board. Drive nails to bring the panel tight to framing, then strike each nail one more time to "dimple" (set) the head, taking care not to break face paper.

Wall application and corners

In horizontal application, bottom panels are installed first; the second row can then be rested on the first. Nails are spaced 7 in. apart and dimpled. No nail in the top course should be less than 7 in. from the ceiling. If adhesive is used, no nails in the field are required unless a panel is bowed—then it may be nailed temporarily while adhesive sets. In a vertical corner, the panel edge that is lapped over need not be nailed.

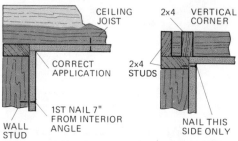

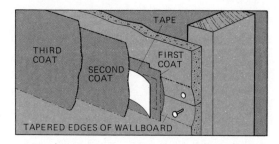

Finishing joints

Joints are filled, reinforced and finished as shown. First coat of joint compound is applied with 4-in. joint knife and tape pressed into it with knife held at 45° angle. Allow at least 24 hours for each coat to dry. Second and third coats are sanded and third feathered-out with 10-in. joint knife to a total width of 12 to 14 in. Treat end and butt joints the same way, with final coat 14 to 18 in. wide. Nailheads get three sanded coats of compound, no tape unless paper is broken.

Finishing corners

Two coats of compound may do for an outside corner. Final coat should extend 7 to 9 in. back from nose of corner. Tape creased lengthwise is embedded in inside corners, topped with one or two feathered coats of compound. To halt cracking, use the least possible compound in crease line.

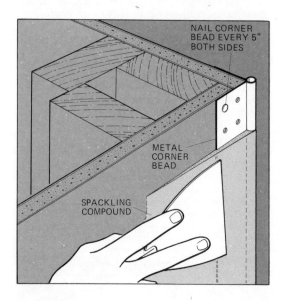

Electricity in the home

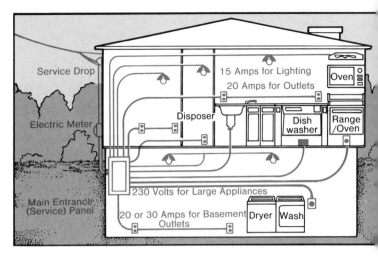

■ THE ELECTRICAL CIRCUITS in a home distribute and control power much like the plumbing system handles the water supply. But instead of pipes, there are wires that carry the electricity. Instead of faucets, there are switches that turn the supply on and off. Instead of sinks and toilets, there are lights, ranges and other appliances that use the power.

Electrical codes

Almost all communities have codes that govern the use of electricity. If a community doesn't have its own code, the National Electrical Code may apply. These codes protect you against misused electrical products and faulty electrical installation techniques that can cause electrical shock and fires. A local code won't prohibit you from repairing a plug on the end of a lamp cord, changing a switch, or replacing a burned-out fuse, but you may need a permit to make wiring changes in your home, such as adding a new circuit to the main electrical entrance.

If the work you do does not comply with local electrical codes, your home insurance may not cover you if an accident occurs. By following the codes, you're a winner in both technology and safety.

Do-it-yourself projects

You can make many electrical repairs yourself without special knowledge or skills. You can even wire new circuits without difficulty if you know something about basic electricity. You'll get a good basic foundation by understanding the material in this explanation of basic electrical wiring. You will put this knowledge to work in remodeling projects you do in the sections about **Home Improvements** in Volume 13, **Basement Remodeling** in Volume 2, and the special section about **Remodeling** in Volume 20. This background will also give you a good base to do the projects in **Appliance Repair** in Volume 1, **Electronic Projects** in Volume 8, and the how-to-do-it projects about **Lamps and Lighting** in Volume 15.

Electricity in the home

Before you start on any projects for electrical repairs or improvements, you should know how electricity comes into your home and how it is divided at the main switch box. Here's a short, simplified course on the subject.

Electricity from a public utility is distributed through electrical substations. You've probably seen them: large rectangular boxes with big wires sticking out the tops. The substations reduce to 2400 volts the original high voltage generated at a dam, an oil- or coal-burning plant, or a nuclear power facility. From the substation, electricity goes to a transformer located on a power pole in your neighborhood.

The transformer then doles out the power to the main switch box in your home at either 115 or 230 volts. In some communities the power may be 120 or 240 volts, but for standard electrical calculations the National Electric Code sets 115/230 volts as the standard rate.

If your public utility is supplying your house with 230-volt service, check the main switch box for a label that specifies the amp service. If you are getting 60 amps, service is in the low range; most electrical codes call for 100-amp service. If you own power tools and large appliances, the system should be upgraded to 150/200 amps.

At your main switch box, the electrical power from the transformer is divided into circuits. One circuit will supply 230 volts to large appliances such as an electric range, a heat pump, and a clothes dryer. The other circuits supply 115 volts to lights and small appliances such as an electric shaver, a food blender, a washing machine, and a television set.

To help understand this better, think of electricity coming from the transformer as a smoothly flowing river between two high banks. At the service entrance of your house, the river is divided into a number of small streams (individual circuits). Each time you plug in an appliance or snap on a switch, you use part of the water from one of these streams. You can use no more water than is in the stream at one time.

At the head of each stream, where it is divided from the main river, is a dam (fuse) by which you can stop the flow. Just ahead of these small dams is a larger dam (main fuse), which can completely stop the flow all at once. In analyzing the wiring in your home, you are making sure that there are enough streams to supply all the appliances you use, and that the streams carry enough to do the job.

Fuses and breakers

Electrical power is controlled by fuses or circuit breakers and by switches. For example, one circuit may supply power to the kitchen and dining room, including the lights, a food blender, the refrigerator, and a can opener. You flip a wall switch and the lights go on; you flip a switch on an appliance and it begins to operate. But suppose all the switches are on at once. If this demands more power than the circuit—the wires—can safely carry, a fuse blows out or a circuit breaker snaps off. This stops the power flow and prevents an overload on the circuit that could start a fire. Overloaded electrical wires build up large amounts of heat; the fuse or circuit breaker is simply a watchdog: When the load is too heavy, the fuse or circuit breaker stops everything before trouble starts.

If fuses blow or circuit breakers pop frequently, it's likely the electrical wiring in your home is not adequate—and inadequate wiring can cause fires.

Switches

The basic types are single-pole and three-way switches, and these can't be interchanged when you are replacing them. Most of the switches are embossed with the letters **AC-DC**, or **AC ONLY**. AC ONLY means the switch may be used only for alternating current, the power furnished by your utility company. AC-DC means the switch can be used in both alternating current and direct current circuits.

These are the types of switches most commonly sold by hardware stores and home centers.

Snap switches make a snapping noise when the toggle is tripped. The snap comes from a spring

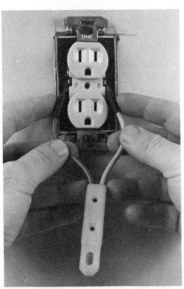

TESTING for power with a voltage tester. Touch one probe of the tester to the positive (power) wire and the other probe to the negative wire. If the bulb in the tester lights, the power is on.

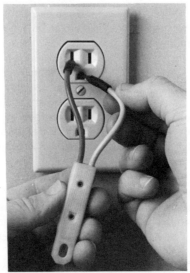

TO CHECK an outlet ground, place one probe of a voltage tester in the grounding slot and the other into the elongated (prong) slots. If the tester does not light, the receptacle is *not grounded* and is dangerous. Check inside wiring.

COVER PLATE grounds are checked by touching one probe of the voltage tester to the cover plate screw and inserting the other probe into the elongated slots. If the tester doesn't light, the cover plate isn't grounded. Check inside wiring.

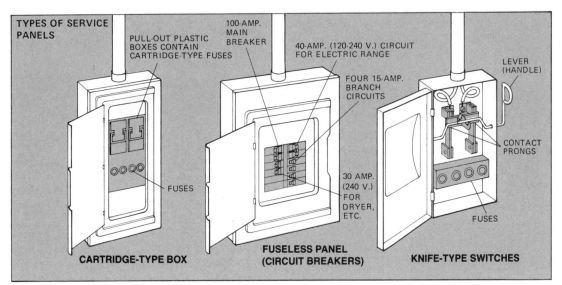

TYPES OF SERVICE PANELS

PULL-OUT PLASTIC BOXES CONTAIN CARTRIDGE-TYPE FUSES

100-AMP. MAIN BREAKER

40-AMP. (120-240 V.) CIRCUIT FOR ELECTRIC RANGE

FOUR 15-AMP. BRANCH CIRCUITS

LEVER (HANDLE)

CONTACT PRONGS

FUSES

30 AMP. (240 V.) FOR DRYER, ETC.

FUSES

CARTRIDGE-TYPE BOX

FUSELESS PANEL (CIRCUIT BREAKERS)

KNIFE-TYPE SWITCHES

IN CARTRIDGE-TYPE BOX (service-entrance panel), the power is shut off by pulling out both of the cartridge cases. The main fuses (cartridge-type) are housed inside this box. The fuses below the main fuses serve branch circuits throughout the house.

FUSELESS service entrance panels are equipped with circuit breakers that handle the main source of power and individual branch circuits. To shut off all power, the main breaker is moved to the OFF position. Circuit toggles control individual circuits.

KNIFE-TYPE SWITCHES are made in several varieties. They usually are found in older wiring systems. To cut the power, move the lever handle to OFF. If the box has fuses in it, each fuse controls one circuit.

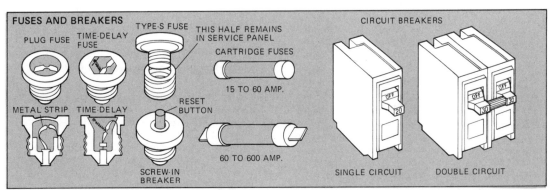

FUSES AND BREAKERS

PLUG FUSE

TIME-DELAY FUSE

TYPE-S FUSE

THIS HALF REMAINS IN SERVICE PANEL

CARTRIDGE FUSES

15 TO 60 AMP.

CIRCUIT BREAKERS

METAL STRIP

TIME-DELAY

RESET BUTTON

60 TO 600 AMP.

SCREW-IN BREAKER

SINGLE CIRCUIT

DOUBLE CIRCUIT

FUSES AND BREAKERS are designed to prevent fire hazards. If a line (circuit) becomes overloaded because its capacity is exceeded by current demand, the fuse controlling that line will "blow." This breaks the link with the main fuse, and the line goes dead. Cartridge and plug type fuses always must be replaced with new fuses. Circuit breakers trip a switch to the OFF position when the line becomes overloaded. You simply flip the toggle to ON to restore the power. Before reactivating a circuit breaker that has tripped, turn off the equipment on that circuit to prevent a surge of power along the line.

that controls the contacts inside the switch. Snap switches are the standard household switch, and usually cost less than other types.

Quiet switches, or mercury switches, do not snap when the toggle is tripped. Quiet switches may be connected to AC-DC systems.

Dimmer switches are designed for either fluorescent or incandescent lighting. They can be used in either single-pole or three-way connections. Dimmers have a rheostat that lets you reduce the wattage used by the lights. There are three types of dimmer switches: high-low, rotary, and push-rotary. A high-low switch has three switch positions: off, low, and high. At the low setting, the light is about half wattage. The high-low is the cheapest type of dimmer switch. The rotary dimmer has a knob that increases or decreases the wattage to the lamp. It may be set to off and up the scale to high. A push-rotary switch, the most expensive type, has a rotary dimmer control and a separate toggle switch. The light may be turned on by pushing in the dimmer

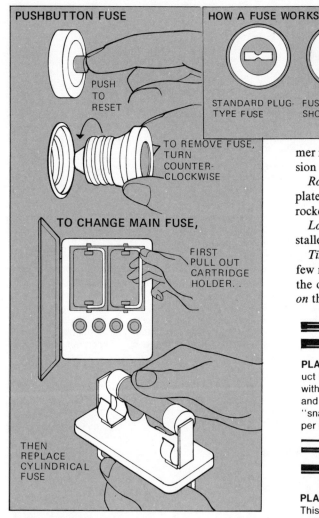

PUSHBUTTON FUSE

PUSH TO RESET

TO REMOVE FUSE, TURN COUNTER-CLOCKWISE

HOW A FUSE WORKS

STANDARD PLUG-TYPE FUSE

FUSE BLOWN BY SHORT CIRCUIT

FUSE BLOWN BY OVERLOAD

BREAKER SWITCHES OFF AUTOMATICALLY

TO CHANGE MAIN FUSE,

FIRST PULL OUT CARTRIDGE HOLDER. .

THEN REPLACE CYLINDRICAL FUSE

TO REPLACE A FUSE, stand on a dry spot (such as a piece of plywood) and keep one hand behind you. A resettable screw-in fuse is reactivated by pushing a button in the center of the fuse. A standard plug-type fuse must be unscrewed, removed, and replaced with a similar fuse of the same amperage. Do not use a higher-rated fuse—even temporarily. The amperage rating is stamped on the bottom metal contact of the fuse. A cartridge-type fuse is replaced by pulling the plastic box housing. If the contacts are corroded, clean them with steel wool and apply a daub of petroleum jelly to the metal ends. This will help deter corrosion.

control or by flipping the toggle.

Before buying a dimmer, check the label on the switch package; it will give you data on the maximum wattage of the light bulbs that can be used with the switch. Dimmers can cause interference with radios, television sets, and stereo sets. You can solve this problem by simply plugging the equipment into a circuit not connected to the dimmer. Power line filters that stop dim-

mer interference are available at radio and television stores.

Rocker switches use almost all of the cover plate as a toggle to turn on and off lights. Some rockers glow in the dark.

Lock switches lock with a key. They are installed the same way as a conventional switch.

Time-delay switches keep a light burning for a few moments after the switch has been turned to the off position. They do not automatically turn *on* the lights.

PLASTIC-SHEATHED CABLE—INDOOR. This product is used for all types of circuits indoors. It is flat, with a tough, flexible outer jacket. It is easy to pull and strip, especially where the wire has to be "snaked" through walls and floors. It has solid-copper conductors.

PLASTIC-SHEATHED CABLE—DUAL-PURPOSE. This cable is made for indoor and outdoor use and underground. It requires no conduit and is flat in shape. Manufactured to resist moisture, acid, and corrosion, the cable may be run through masonry units and between framing.

FLEXIBLE ARMORED CABLE may be used for either exposed runs on wall and ceiling surfaces, or for concealed runs in hollow spaces of walls, floors, and ceilings. It is recommended for use in dry locations only. However it may be embedded in wall or ceiling plaster. Use steel boxes.

RIGID THIN-WALL CONDUIT. This is the most expensive and most generally accepted type of wire covering because it gives greater protection to the wires. It also grounds the entire system for added safety. It may be used inside and outside and through masonry units—except cinder block.

Adjustable time-delay switches may be set to delay the light from being turned off for any period from 45 seconds up to 12 hours. These are similar to the time-delay switches except they have two settings: off and delay.

Time-clock switches automatically turn the lights on and off at prescribed intervals. These switches are costly and may require a deep junction box to provide room for the clockworks.

Special switches not often stocked by home centers and hardware stores include four-way switches that work in tandem with two- and three-way switches to control a light from three locations, and double-pole switches for 230-volt fixtures. Check these switches before buying: double-pole and four-way switches look alike.

Wire terminals are found in different locations on the switches; check your installation before buying switches.

Side-wired switches have terminal screws on one side only. Front-wired switches have terminal screws on the front of the switch—one on top and one on the bottom. End-wired switches have terminals on the top and bottom. Back-wired switches have holes in the back into which short lengths of bare wire are inserted. Next to the wire holes are small slots; if you want to remove the wires, you release the spring clamp that holds the wire by pushing a screwdriver into the slot. Some back-wired switches also have terminal screws on the side of the switch. Three-way back-wired switches have a hole marked COM; this is the power wire connection.

Outlets

The three basic receptacles, or outlets, commonly stocked by home centers and hardware stores are described below. Special receptacles such as a receptacle-and-switch combination may also be found at electrical stores.

Grounded receptacles have three slots for a three-prong, or grounded plug. One slot is connected to the positive (hot) wire, one to the negative wire, and the third to the ground wire. According to the codes, no new wiring may be installed without a ground wire. Standard grounded receptacles are side-wired with a top or bottom grounding terminal.

Back-wired receptacles are wired like back-wired switches.

Polarized receptacles have one wide and one narrow slot. The plug on a polarized appliance has one prong wider than the other, so it fits only into a polarized receptacle. The purpose of this system is to prevent electrical shock. You can't

DIMMER SWITCHES lower the wattage supplied to lamps when a control knob is turned. The shaft for the friction-fitted knob is seen here in the center of the switch. On this model the light may be turned on and off by pushing the knob down. After a dimmer switch has been wired into a standard junction box, as shown here, a cover plate slips over the shaft and is fastened with screws.

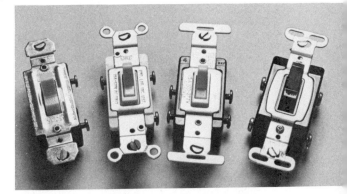

TYPES OF SWITCHES that fasten to wall junction boxes include, from left: single-pole; three-way; four-way; and double-pole. You can tell the difference by the number of terminals on the switch. The four-way and double-pole switches look alike but usually are labeled.

insert the plug the wrong way into the receptacle; therefore, the grounding system reduces the shock hazard.

How switches and outlets are sold. Switches and outlets are marked as to power capacities and other data, and most of them bear a UL listing. Standard colors are black, dark brown, and ivory.

Standard cover plates are available to cover the switches and outlets in the same standard colors. You can also buy decorative plates. Plates also may be painted to match room colors, or they may be covered with wallpaper, contact paper, and decorative tape.

TWO BASIC TYPES of outlets are (at top) a polarized outlet with one slot larger than the other and (at bottom) a three-pronged outlet that accepts a grounded or three-pronged plug. A polarized outlet accepts only a plug with prongs of different sizes in order to properly ground the fixture in the outlet.

Electrical Wire

Electrical wire falls into several classifications and sub-classifications. Type T wire (T for thermoplastic insulation) is used for residential wiring. *Type T* is a general classification under which are these sub-classifications:

Types of wire. Type **NW** is only for indoor use under dry conditions. Type **UF** is for sheltered outdoor use. Type **TW** is for outdoor use where damp and wet conditions prevail. Type **SPT** is only for lamp cord. Type **HPN** or **HPD** is only for heater cord.

Bell wire must be used only in doorbell circuits. It's rated for 25 amps. *Speaker wire* must be used only for wiring radio and phonograph speakers.

Type **AC** cable is used where codes require metal-clad wire. Type **CO-ALR** is aluminum wire that must be used only with 15- and 20-amp aluminum fixtures. Type **CU-AL** is aluminum wire for ratings larger than 20 amps.

Caution: Always use aluminum wire with aluminum fixtures. Never connect aluminum wire to copper terminals or copper wire to aluminum terminals. Connecting different metals causes a corrosive action

that can lead to an electrical fire.

Wire numbers. The size of electrical wire is identified by the numbers in the AWG (American Wire Gauge) system. (It has nothing to do with wire type). The larger the number, the smaller the size of the wire and the lower the amp rating. For example, No. 18 wire is small in diameter and can carry only 7 amps. No. 10 wire is larger and carries 30 amps. Here's a complete list:

No. 18 wire	7 amps
No. 16 wire	10 amps
No. 14 wire	15 amps
No. 12 wire	20 amps
No. 10 wire	30 amps
No. 8 wire	40 amps
No. 6 wire	55 amps

You'll often see the AWG number stamped on the insulation of wires along with the type.

In fusing or ciruit breaker systems, use Nos. 16 and 18 wire in a 15-amp circuit, Nos. 10 and 12 wire in a 20-amp circuit, and Nos. 8 and 10 wire in a 30-amp circuit.

For general repair and improvement work, use Nos. 14, 12, and 10 wire. Do not use Nos. 16 and 18 wire except for low-voltage systems such as lamp cords, doorbell wire, speaker systems and intercom systems.

Use No. 14 and 12 wire for 120-volt circuits. Use No. 10 wire for 120-volt circuits to which heavy appliances such as refrigerators, window airconditioners and power tools are connected. Use No. 8 and No. 6 wire for 230/240-volt circuits.

How wire is constructed. The electrical codes in your community probably permit three varieties of wire construction.

Plastic sheathed cable comes in **NW** and **UF** types. It's ideal for the do-it-yourselfer because it is highly flexible and may be snaked through walls, around corners, up, down, and through foundations.

Flexible armored cable—sometimes called **BX** — is **NW** type; it must not be used in damp locations. This product has a shiny galvanized metal sheath through which the power wires run. Armored cable is easy for the do-it-yourselfer to use since it can be snaked.

Before you buy flexible armored cable, however, check your local codes; some codes prohibit its use anywhere.

Thin-wall rigid conduit looks like galvanized steel water pipe without the threaded ends. This product is only a sheathing for the wires that you thread through it—such as flexible plastic-sheathed.

Rigid conduit is approved by most codes, although it's smart to check the codes before buying.

Conduit is frequently used for new electrical wir-

HIGH-VOLTAGE, heavy-duty appliance cords have special plug and outlet shapes so they can't be connected to the wrong circuit. When buying replacements, take the old cord to the store to buy the right item.

A WATERPROOF BOX has seamless joints and cable openings that are threaded to keep out water. Gaskets are inserted between the receptacle and the box covering, and inside the small doors to keep moisture out.

ing; it is difficult to use in some applications simply because it is rigid. You can buy connections (couplings and elbows and offsets) for the straight conduit. Conduit also may be bent—with a conduit bender—to gentle curves and slight angles.

Stranded and solid wire. Inside insulated wire you'll find two kinds of wire: stranded and solid.

Stranded wire is made up of many very thick hairlike wires twisted and wound together. It is intended only for lamp and appliance cords that are moved frequently subjecting the wire to repeated bending that could cause a solid wire to break. It is usually found in AWG Number 18, although some heavy-duty appliance cord stranded wire can be found in larger sizes.

Solid wire has just one solid wire in AWG Numbers 8 through 18. In wires numbered 0 through 6, you'll find multiples of solid wire encased in the insulation.

WIRE SIZES are identified by number. The larger the number, the smaller the wire. No. 18 wire is available both as stranded wire and as a solid wire. Bell cord is solid wire for low-voltage systems. Match wire size to the volts and amps the circuit carries.

WIRES ARE MARKED FOR USE as required by local codes. Power wires have black or white insulation; ground wires may be bare or have red or green insulation.

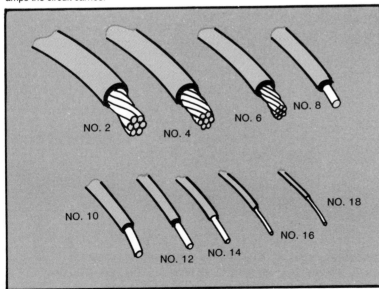

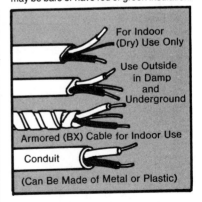

THREE-WIRE CONNECTIONS for either an additional fuse panel or safety switch are installed this way. The power take-off lugs, available in most entrance panels, permit partial extensions of existing wiring without installation of a larger entrance switch to handle the electricity.

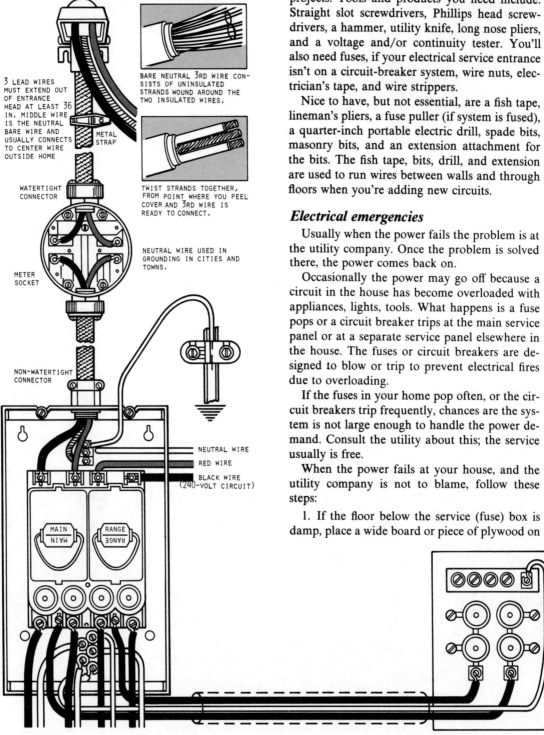

3 LEAD WIRES MUST EXTEND OUT OF ENTRANCE HEAD AT LEAST 36 IN. MIDDLE WIRE IS THE NEUTRAL BARE WIRE AND USUALLY CONNECTS TO CENTER WIRE OUTSIDE HOME

METAL STRAP

BARE NEUTRAL 3RD WIRE CONSISTS OF UNINSULATED STRANDS WOUND AROUND THE TWO INSULATED WIRES.

WATERTIGHT CONNECTOR

TWIST STRANDS TOGETHER, FROM POINT WHERE YOU PEEL COVER AND 3RD WIRE IS READY TO CONNECT.

METER SOCKET

NEUTRAL WIRE USED IN GROUNDING IN CITIES AND TOWNS.

NON-WATERTIGHT CONNECTOR

NEUTRAL WIRE
RED WIRE
BLACK WIRE (240-VOLT CIRCUIT)

MAIN

RANGE

Electrical tools and products

A basic electrical tool kit doesn't need to be elaborate or costly. In fact, you probably have many of the necessary tools. The basic kit can be expanded as you get into specialized electrical projects. Tools and products you need include: Straight slot screwdrivers, Phillips head screwdrivers, a hammer, utility knife, long nose pliers, and a voltage and/or continuity tester. You'll also need fuses, if your electrical service entrance isn't on a circuit-breaker system, wire nuts, electrician's tape, and wire strippers.

Nice to have, but not essential, are a fish tape, lineman's pliers, a fuse puller (if system is fused), a quarter-inch portable electric drill, spade bits, masonry bits, and an extension attachment for the bits. The fish tape, bits, drill, and extension are used to run wires between walls and through floors when you're adding new circuits.

Electrical emergencies

Usually when the power fails the problem is at the utility company. Once the problem is solved there, the power comes back on.

Occasionally the power may go off because a circuit in the house has become overloaded with appliances, lights, tools. What happens is a fuse pops or a circuit breaker trips at the main service panel or at a separate service panel elsewhere in the house. The fuses or circuit breakers are designed to blow or trip to prevent electrical fires due to overloading.

If the fuses in your home pop often, or the circuit breakers trip frequently, chances are the system is not large enough to handle the power demand. Consult the utility about this; the service usually is free.

When the power fails at your house, and the utility company is not to blame, follow these steps:

1. If the floor below the service (fuse) box is damp, place a wide board or piece of plywood on

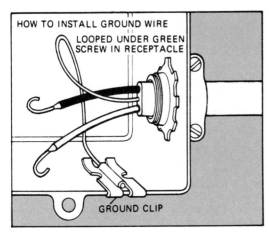

HOW TO INSTALL GROUND WIRE
LOOPED UNDER GREEN
SCREW IN RECEPTACLE

GROUND CLIP

GROUNDING IS REQUIRED if you are using nonmetallic cable. The ground connects from a green screw to a ground clip mounted on the junction box. The screw is on the receptacle. Loop the wire around it, turn down the screw, and tie off the wire in the grounding clip.

the floor under the entrance and stand on it. It's a good idea to have such a board stored near the power entrance for emergencies. The wood isolates you from the damp flooring and protects against electrical shock.

2. If the house is on a circuit-breaker system, snap the toggles of the breaker to the "on" position. You may have to do this a couple of times to restore the power. If so, the toggle is faulty and should be replaced.

3. If the house is on a fuse system, put one hand in your hip pocket or behind you and turn out the blown fuse with your other hand. If the fuse is a cartridge type product, use a fuse puller to remove and replace it.

Many appliances—especially washers, dryers, and ranges—may have a separate fusing system built into them. They may be receiving power but still won't work. If this is the case, try pushing the "reset" button on the appliance. It will be marked as such and usually is located on the main control panel of the appliance.

Some electric ranges have a fuse system. This fuse usually is located in the top rear of the oven compartment or under one of the rear elements on top of the range.

Caution: Always replace a fuse with a new fuse of the same amperage. The amperage is stamped on the conductor at the bottom of the fuse: "15," "20," or "30." A smaller fuse size may cause the fuse to continually pop; a larger fuse size may not pop when the circuit is overloaded.

If you live in an older home, there may be more than one central power service entrance. This often is the case where a clothes dryer or electric range has been added. More power is

necessary for these appliances, so a separate fuse system (usually a circuit breaker) was installed to handle the extra load. If changing fuses and tripping circuit breakers at the main power entrance doesn't restore power, be sure to look elsewhere for another fuse box or circuit breaker. The trouble may be in this power entrance.

Wire sizes are important

Different sizes of electrical wires carry different amounts of electricity. Each size is designated by a number, and the smaller the number, the larger the wire. Generally, most lighting circuits are wired with No. 14 wire. Most appliance circuits are wired with No. 12 wire and sometimes with No. 10 wire.

Wire offers resistance to the electricity passing through it. The larger the diameter of the wire the less the resistance. Resistance creates heat, and the more resistance, the greater the heat. When you draw too much current through a small wire by plugging in too many appliances, you generate considerable heat—enough, in fact, to create a fire hazard. The insulation melts off the wires.

While the National Electrical Code permits the use of No. 14 wire in lighting circuits, some local codes demand that No. 12 be the smallest wire used. The additional capacity of No. 12 is an extra margin of safety.

These specifications refer to copper wire. If aluminum wire is used, always install one size larger—No. 12 and No. 10. The wire will be designated with the letters CO-ALR for 15- and 20-amps and CU-AL for higher power ratings. Always make sure that the terminals of switches, outlets, and other fixtures are so marked. Mixing copper wire with aluminum terminals—or copper terminals with aluminum wire—can set up corrosion and cause trouble. Also, make sure terminal screws are especially tight on aluminum wires. Aluminum tends to expand and contract, which loosens the screws and therefore causes poor electrical contact.

When buying wire, keep this formula in mind: 0 to 4 gauge wire for transformer to service entrance hookups; 6 to 14 gauge wire for electrical circuit hookups.

Wires have different colored insulation for a purpose. Black and colored wires (usually red) are "hot" or power wires. They carry current. White wires are neutral or ground wires. Green wires also are ground wires. The present wiring in your home follows this color coding, and when you install new wiring, you should follow the color code. It will make the job go easier.

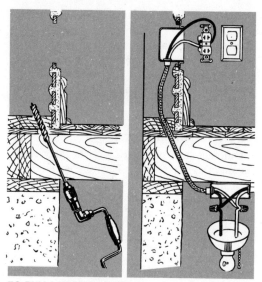

TO RUN A WIRE through a floor, first select the outlet site and cut an opening through the wall covering. Bore a diagonal hole up from the basement or crawl space. Then push a short length of fish wire up from the lower level with wires attached, and pull the wires through to the outlet opening. Use armored or sheathed cable.

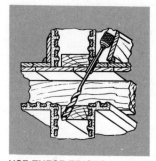
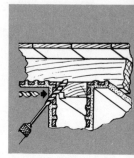

USE THESE TRICKS to fish a wire through floors and ceilings. If you can get into the room above, remove the baseboard and drill a diagonal hole downward. Then drill a hole upward from below. Special auger bits help bore holes for fishing power wires.

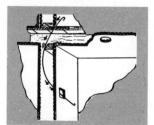
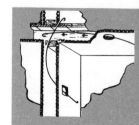

PUSH THE FISH WIRE, hooked at the ends, through the hole on the second floor. Pull one end out at the switch or outlet opening. Then push the wire through a ceiling outlet. Fish until you hook the first wire. Electrical fish wires are made in several lengths; 12- and 20-ft. are best.

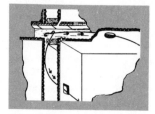
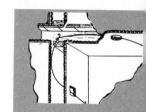

PULL EITHER WIRE until both are hooked. Then pull both wires until the hooks meet. Finally, pull the shorter wire through the switch outlet. When the hook from the long wire appears, attach the cable and pull it through. Make sure the cable is attached tightly to the fish wire.

The National Electrical Code also has a formula for determining how many circuits are needed in a home. First, find the square footage of your home, using the outside dimensions of the foundation. Include the area of each floor in use, and also the areas like the basement and attic which may not be in use now but might at sometime in the future.

The code calls for a minimum of 3 watts available for each sq. ft. of space. This means that a standard 15-amp. circuit delivering 1725 watts can serve 600 sq. ft. If you divide the total square footage of your home by 600, you will find the minimum number of lighting circuits required.

Note that this figure is *minimum,* and refers to lighting circuits only. If you are to have ample wiring with some room for growth, divide the square footage by 400. Thus, if your home is 2400 sq. ft., you should have a minimum of four lighting circuits, but six circuits would be much better.

In addition to the lighting circuits, the code also requires that you have at least two appliance circuits, each rated at 20 amps, and wired with No. 12 wire. No lights are included in these circuits, which are intended for small appliance outlets only. The circuits must serve the kitchen, dining room, laundry, family room, and breakfast area, where you use most of the appliances.

Both of these circuits must extend to the kitchen.

In determining adequate wiring for your home, a good rule of thumb is to figure an appliance circuit for each 500 sq. ft. You also should keep in mind the areas of heavy appliance use, such as a workshop, laundry area, etc. In a home of 2400 sq. ft., five appliance circuits would assure good safe wiring.

Planning for new wiring

Draw an electrical diagram of your home, first because you should have a chart of the circuits for handy reference, and second, to use in determining whether or not your wiring is adequate.

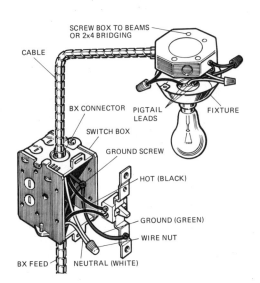

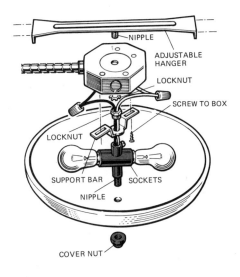

HERE'S HOW to install a fixture switch. Be sure that you connect black wires to black wires, white to white, and ground to ground from switch to the fixture.

A TYPICAL FIXTURE is assembled this way. The hanger spans the joists and supports the assembly. It is adjustable so the assembly is easy to install between framing members. If a hanger isn't used, the box is screwed or nailed to the joist for support.

Begin by counting the fuses in the service box to find the number of circuits. Then learn what lights and outlets are on each circuit.

One way to do this is to turn on all lights, then unscrew the fuses one at a time. Note which lights go out. Check wall outlets the same way by

A THREE-WAY SWITCH that controls a fixture from two points is wired this way. The box connections will be easy if you study this diagram before you start. For strength, wrap the wire nut connections with plastic electrician's tape.

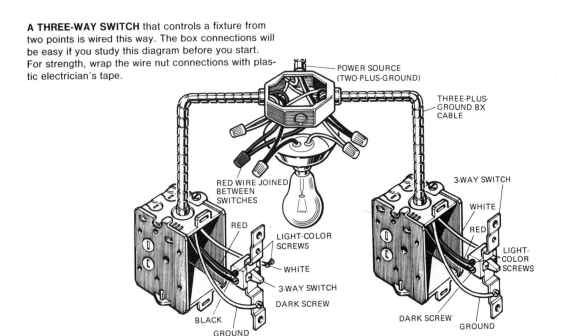

plugging table lamps into them.

Draw a plan of each floor, locating all lights, outlets and switches. Use colored pencils to join the outlets and lights on each circuit. Finally, number each circuit, and tape the numbers near the corresponding fuses in the service box.

Now survey the chart and answer these questions:

• Do you have at least as many circuits as required by national or local codes?

• Do you have enough circuits for really good wiring?

• Are there at least two appliance circuits?

• Are there individual circuits for such heavy-duty appliances as electric ranges, water heaters, the furnace, air conditioning, clothes dryer?

You may have to slightly rework your initial plan. If so, here are several rules to follow:

1. Plan a wall outlet for every 12 ft. of wall in the house. For convenience, have at least three in each room, more if the room is large.

2. One lighting circuit might include two small bedrooms and a bathroom, or a large bedroom and a bathroom or walk-in closet.

3. Don't put all the lights on one floor on one circuit. If that fuse blows, you're out of light.

4. Living room and kitchen lights can be on one circuit since the power demand isn't too great.

5. Dining room and hall lights may be put on one circuit, along with a powder room.

6. One appliance circuit should start in the kitchen and have outlets in the dining room and breakfast or family rooms. Another appliance circuit should serve the kitchen only.

7. Plan separate appliance circuits for the laundry and workshop areas.

8. Plan separate circuits for individual major appliances. Some of the appliances may require 230 v. instead of 115 v.

Now plan the changes you want to make, along with the new circuits. Check the service box. Does it have empty fuse sockets or unused panels for circuit breakers? If not, you can buy an additional service box which can be mounted alongside the present one. There usually are lugs in the present box from which you can wire the service to the new box. Simply knock out the lugs with a punch. Also check the use to which you are putting your present circuits. If you are over-using some of them, plan to cut them in half, providing two circuits and two fuses or circuit breaker toggles.

At this point, you can make a diagram of the house as it will be after you have made the wiring

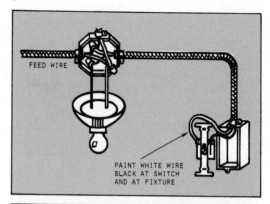

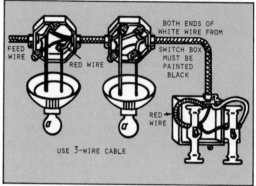

WHEN 3-WIRE CABLE is required (specified "14/3 With Ground"), the white wire from the switch must be painted or somehow tagged "black" at the switch and at the outlet. This code lets you know that the wire is "hot."

changes. Plan your work in easy steps, and make a list of the materials you will need for the job.

Wire buymanship

Most electrical codes permit three kinds of wire. Most retailers sell all three kinds:

Flexible armored cable, sometimes known as BX, is good for rewiring a home because of its flexibility. It is easy to run through existing walls. It cannot, however, be used in damp locations, outside, or underground. And some local codes do not permit its use anywhere.

Plastic sheathed cable is very flexible and excellent when you must "snake" wire through existing walls. However, care must be taken when working with it not to damage the plastic covering.

Thin-wall rigid conduit is the most acceptable

type of wiring system. Wires are threaded through it. Most new work is done with conduit, and many communities require it because it does the best job of protecting the wires it carries, and because the entire system is grounded. It is difficult, however, to use in remodeling work.

Wire is known by *type* and is stamped as such. Type AC cable is used where codes specify that the wires must be metal-clad. Type NM cable is the plastic sheathed cable described above. Unless it is otherwise specified by local codes, Type NM cable should be used indoors under dry conditions. Type UF cable may be used underground or in wet and corrosive areas. Do not expose UF cable to sunlight.

In rewiring your home, or remodeling the wiring, your big buy in wire will be Type NM with two- or three-wire configurations. Conductor sizes will include No. 14, No. 12, and, probably No. 10. The cable will have a ground wire—usually bare without insulation.

The color codes on Type NM will be:
• One black, one white, and one bare wire in two-wire cable.
• One black, one white, one red, one blue and one bare in four-wire cable.

Type SPT is lamp cord. You know it by its shape: a groove runs down the center of both wires so the wires may be split. The wires also are stranded, not solid, as in Types NM, UF, HPN, and so forth. Wire usually is sold by the roll: 25-, 50,- and 100-ft.

Working with electricity

"Work safe" are the key words in making any electrical repairs or improvements. Note the following precautions before you start any job:

1. Do not work on any switch or outlet until you have disconnected the circuit by tripping the circuit breaker or unscrewing the fuse.

2. When working at the service box, pull out the main fuse, completely disconnecting the box from the incoming power lines.

3. Double-check your work before restoring the power to the circuit.

Take time to study the service box. Note that wires come in from a transformer. The wires are black, red, and white. Each of the colored wires carries 115 v. The white wire is neutral.

The black and red wires are connected to the main fuses or circuit breakers, while the white wire is connected to a copper bar, which is grounded to a cold water pipe. If you pull the main plastic fuse box out, you will find in it two red fuses that look similar to shotgun shells.

When the box is pulled out, all electricity is shut OFF. When it is pushed back in place, the current is ON. Some service boxes have just a toggle that is switched to turn the power on and off.

Each of the individual fuses or circuit breakers is connected to the main fuse. If the wiring is visible, you can see that the connection is made with a black wire. A white wire connects each individual fuse to the grounding bar.

You may find several lugs or big screws near the fuses. These are the points at which you attach the wiring when you install another service box. Many service boxes have what appears to be a second main fuse, usually marked "Range." This is the fuse for a 230-volt circuit, and both incoming hot wires are connected to it, while only one of the incoming wires is connected to the other main fuse. If you live in an older home, the "Range" circuit may be in another service box near the main service box.

Adding new circuits

If you have enough empty fuse sockets for additional circuits, follow this procedure when wiring a circuit to the service box:

1. Pull the main fuse to turn off the power.

2. Select a "knock-out" plug near the fuse to be used and knock it out with a punch.

3. Fasten the connector to the circuit wire. Thread the connector into the hole, thread on a locknut and tighten it. There should be about 8 in. of wire in the box.

4. Strip the ends of the wire and form a hook on the end of each wire. Hook the black wire under the screw at the fuse socket. Put the white wire under the screw on the grounding bar. Tighten the screws (terminals).

5. Insert the main fuse in the box. The power is now on. Now screw in a 15-amp fuse or set the circuit breaker.

If the service entrance is a circuit breaker—not fuse—arrangement, you will have to pry out an escutcheon plate where a new circuit breaker toggle will be inserted. There are two types. One simply snaps into the space and is secured by friction of the toggle housing. The other type has a plug-in device. By turning off the power and removing an existing toggle, you can determine the type the circuit breaker utilizes.

1. Slip the white neutral wire and bare grounding wire into the slot in the box and fasten it to the neutral bar. Pull on it to make sure it is secure and the holding screw is properly tightened.

2. Hook the black power wire to the circuit

breaker. There is a screw on the toggle device for this.

3. Slip the toggle breaker in the appropriate slot so it "clicks" or is secure in the slot.

4. Turn on the main breaker toggle and check the circuit.

When the job is complete, and if you have complied with the electrical code in your community, have an inspector check your work. The inspector's okay means the work is satisfactory and the system probably complies with insurance regulations.

Making wire connections

The wiring systems that may be used in residences usually consist of either flexible-armor type or non-metallic sheathed cable with a ground wire which may be insulated or bare. These wiring systems should not be intermixed. For example, if your home is wired with flexible armor type cable, stick with this cable. Regardless of the wiring type you use, the basic techniques for joining (splicing) these wires are the same.

• Stripping and cutting wire is best done with a combination tool that both cuts and strips clean the most common sizes of stranded and solid wire. A button on the handle lets you set the jaws to the desired wire gauge so you can remove the insulation without breaking the wires.

About ½-inch of insulation should be removed from the wire to expose this conductor. Try to shape the insulation like a sharpened pencil rather than a blunt cut. The nose of the stripping tool can be used to form the loop or hook on the wire so the wire may be properly fastened under the terminal screws on the outlet or switch you're wiring.

• After the wire is bared and bent into a hook, fit it around the terminal screw in the direction the terminal screw turns—usually clockwise.

This way, when the terminal screw is tightened it also tightens the wire under the screw. If the wire is installed backward, the wire is likely to back out as the screw is tightened down. This results in a poor connection.

• To join wire at prewired fixtures, such as a ceiling light, use solderless connectors. They often are called "wire nuts." The connectors are plastic caps with a threaded metal insert that let you "screw" the wires together in a connection.

After the wires are bared and inserted into the cap and twisted, give the wires a slight tug to make sure the connector won't slip off. It's also a good idea to wrap plastic electrical tape around the connector and wires for added strength.

• Ground wires are required by codes if the wire is nonmetallic cable.

Receptacles must be grounded from a green screw or a ground clip; both are mounted on the junction box.

To make this connection, the bared ground wire is looped under the green screw and then pushed through the ground clip.

It is important that all systems are grounded throughout. If you miss one ground connection, you break the entire connection.

Working with cable

Wiring with plastic or metallic cable is just as easy as wiring with other types of wire. Here are several tips to help you do jobs easier and safer:

• There is no "multiple choice" question in wiring. If you have any doubts about which wire goes where, don't guess. Call in a professional.

• Always buy UI-approved, sheathed, copper wiring. It may be packaged in armored metallic cable (type AC) or thermoplastic cable (type TW or THW). These letter symbols are embossed on the cable's outer surface.

For 15-ampere circuits, use No. 14 gauge wire. For 20-ampere circuits, use No. 12 gauge wire. Each size should have a third grounding wire. This is specified in the store by "14/2 With Ground." Or "12/2 With Ground."

• Follow the color codes when you are joining new conductors to existing ones. Black wires are always connected to black wires; white wires go to white wires. Green or bare wires go to their counterparts.

The coding is very important since in house wiring the white always acts as the grounded neutral conductor, the black as the power wire, and the bare or green wire as the safety grounding conductor that protects you from electrical shock.

• If you plan to install a new junction box or take a new line out of an existing box, be sure to attach the grounding wire to the metal box. If two or more sets of conductors are connected in the box, connect the two grounding wires together in addition to attaching them to the metal frame. One break in the line can cancel out the safety factor along the entire circuit.

• Always run the black or power conductor (wire) through the switch, never the white wire. If you switch the white instead, the fixture on the circuit will be a permanent, hot, shock hazard—even when the switch is turned off.

• In three-way switching, controlling one light from two different locations, buy two three-way switches and cable specified as "14/3 With

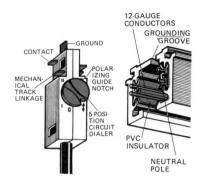

SINGLE AND triple-circuit track has dial settings on a three-circuit system that will activate any combination of lamps.

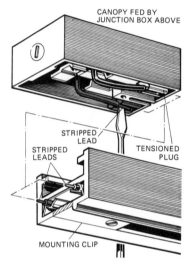

CANOPY BOXES, wired at the ceiling, serve as plugs for the different track sections.

Ground." All necessary wires are in the cable.

Adding a wall outlet

Rooms in older homes never seem to have enough electrical outlets, and many times a long extension cord is used to plug in a lamp across the room.

Although it may look difficult, adding a new outlet is an easy job. Here are the steps:

1. Trace the outlet box on the wall between wall studs. The box should be the same height as the others above the floor. Use a 2½-in.-deep box; all boxes are the same width and height.

Use the box as a template and trace its outline on the wall. You can locate the wall studs by tapping on the wall and listening for a solid sound. Or use a magnetic stud finder.

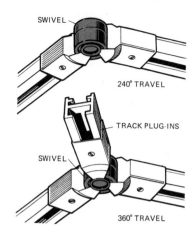

THESE CONNECTORS, and a six-point swivel for track in any direction, are the features of these connectors. The lights simply ride in the channels.

If the wall is lath and plaster, chip away a small hole in the center of the outline to expose a lath so the template can be centered over a full lath. This will provide better strength.

If the box will be fastened to paneling, you can buy a box with special clamps that grip the panels for support. If the wall is lath and plaster, the box is fastened to the wood lath with small screws. If the wall is plasterboard, the box is anchored in the hole with special metal supports.

2. For plasterboard walls, trace around the box and drill two ½-in. holes through the wall at the top and bottom half-round notches.

Then cut the opening with a hand-held hacksaw blade or a keyhole saw. You can protect your hands from the teeth of the saw blade by wrapping the grip with a couple of twists of plastic electrician's tape.

3. You may use armored cable or plastic cable to wire the new outlet. You must cut the armored cable with a hacksaw; the plastic cable may be cut with a sharp utility knife.

Codes require that the wire and box be grounded. If you use armored cable, the metal covering serves as the ground. If you use plastic cable, the third or "ground" wire inside the insulation must be connected to the outlet box with a screw and/or special clip made for this purpose.

4. Strip off the insulation about ½-in. from the black and white wires. Then form a hook on the ends of the bared wires and connect the hook to the terminals of the outlet. The black wire should be hooked to the brass terminal, and the white wire to the light-colored terminal. Also, the hooks should go onto the terminals the direction the terminal screws turn—usually clockwise.

If you are making any other connections inside

the box or along the circuit remember that black wires are always connected to black wires and white wires are always connected to white wires.

5. How you run the cable from an existing box to a new one depends on where the boxes are.

If they're on the same wall, remove the baseboard, notch each stud to accept the cable, and cover the wire with metal kickplates for protection.

If the boxes are on different walls and there is a basement or crawl space below, it's easier to bore up into the walls from underneath and run the cable across under the joists.

If the new outlet is on the other side of a doorway, the cable can be concealed behind the trim. You may have to chip out the plaster or wallboard and run up and over the door. When reinstalling the trim, be careful not to nail through the cable.

To connect the cable to an old box, punch open a knockout port and fish a thin wire through this hole to pull the cable into the box.

Installing a surface switch

If you want to install a new wall switch but don't want to cut into the wall covering, you can use a surface switch, provided there is an existing receptacle nearby. The system is UL-listed.

The system has three adhesive-backed components that are pressed against the wall. A plug-in, solid-state relay transformer (power unit) is set next to an existing single-gang receptacle. The unit is connected with 15 feet of .005-in.-thick two-wire conductor tape, and a clear plastic, wafer-thin touchbutton switch completes the hook-up.

The power unit steps down 110-120v. power to a 2-v. level, claimed to be so safe that if you cut into the wire the extremely low voltage would not be felt as an electrical shock.

An alternate design, using the conductor tape and switch as before, has a separate power unit installed inside a double-gang wall receptacle or ceiling fixture outlet. Extra touchbuttons may be obtained for multiple switching.

Tracking light where it's needed

Track lighting is the answer to illuminating an entire room without putting a 200-watt bulb in the middle of the ceiling. Track lights also may be used for spotlighting, depending on the fixture.

Installing track lighting is simple. One junction box, for example, can feed a series of tracks. You can hang fixtures from the tracks that will throw exactly the light you want.

Track lighting frees you from the limitation of having one outlet box near every source of light. It also lets you make a mistake or change your mind. When you sink a lot of money into an elaborate center-ceiling fixture, that's it. The light is going to stay there. But if you don't like the way your tracks look, just unplug them from the supply box and make a different arrangement. You can also slide fixtures along the track, bunch them at either end, or put different fixtures (throwing different kinds of light) on different tracks altogether. The possibilities are endless.

The system starts at the feed box.

This box is small, matching the contour and style of the track that sits on the ceiling and connects to the junction box above it. Once this is installed, wiring the rest of the system is easy.

Since conductors run the full length of the track, power is available at each end. There are caps (made to close off one end if you're hanging only one track) and connectors (elbows and straights) that let you plug one track into another and continue the system in any direction.

Measure from a side wall and snap a line where the track will be. Small mounting clips are screwed into the ceiling and tracks slip onto them. These clips make installation easy and space the track about ¼ in. off the ceiling to absorb the margin of high or low spots that could make the track uneven.

Two types of track are available. Most basic and easiest to install is a single-circuit track fed with a standard three-wire cable (hot, neutral, and ground). You can control it with two-or three-way switches.

All lamps on this track will go off and on at the same time. But they also make three-circuit track with hardware to match. This system links three separately switched circuits with each length of track. It's ideal in a large room where you can install continuous tracks to cover the entire area.

A light you can't see? This sounds impossible, but it's a special effect from a newly developed fixture. You can look directly into this light from six inches away without squinting. It throws a wide beam of clean white light, but you can't see where the beam is coming from.

The effect is both dramatic and mystifying.

Objects appear to be lighting themselves. The light source is a clear bulb with a silver bowl covering half its outer skin. Light bounces up into a mottled, high-purity, aluminum bowl and is diffused down onto the room. The fixture is generally referred to as "no-glare" lighting.

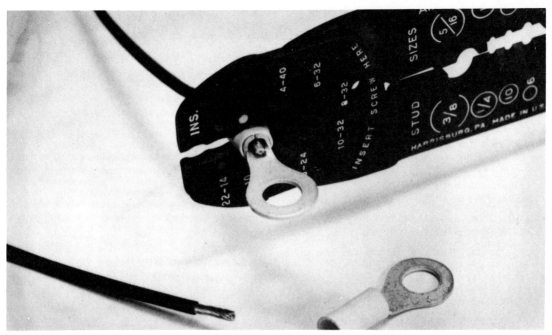

A QUICK SQUEEZE and you've permanently fastened an eye-type connector to a wire end without any soldering. This tool has an extra-large crimping notch near the center for auto-ignition cables.

Crimp-on connectors

■ THE FASTEST WAY to join two wires or attach a connector is with a crimping tool. If you don't believe it, try one of these handy, inexpensive aids the next time you install a light fixture or hook up speaker leads to your stereo.

Crimp-on connectors not only save time over soldering, but handle jobs where soldering could be difficult. When working with heavy wire, for instance, the metal draws heat away so fast it's hard to make a good soldered connection with a light-duty iron. Crimped connectors eliminate the problem. They come in a variety of types and sizes. Many have color-coded insulation sleeves for quick identification of wire gauge. Yellow is used for heavy 10 to 12-gauge wire, blue for medium 14 to 16-gauge wire and red for light 18

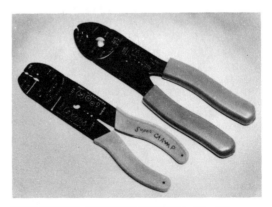

TWO TYPICAL CRIMPING TOOLS handle wire gauges from 10 to 22, and cut and strip ends.

3 TYPES OF CRIMP-ON CONNECTORS FOR EASY WIRE SPLICING

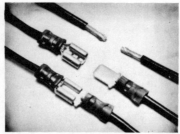

THE BELL-SHAPED SPLICER at the left works like a wire nut except you crimp it on tightly instead of just screwing it on. All you do is twist the wires, slip on the connector and squeeze. At the center, a slip-together coupling can be quickly disconnected if necessary. At the right is a permanent end-to-end splice.

to 22-gauge wire. Some crimping tools have similarly color-coded crimping notches so you can tell at a glance which notch to use depending on the wire diameter you're working with.

HANDY KITS include the crimping tool, assorted connectors and instructions in a plastic carrying case.

BOLT-SHEARING SLOTS are helpful when you don't have the right length on hand and can't get to a store.

Open-ended spade lugs are good for making quick connections to screw terminals since they can be slipped on or off with only a few turns of a screwdriver. Closed-ended eyes can't pull off accidentally, but take a little longer to install since the screw must be removed completely and inserted through the hole. Spades are best for connections that may be changed frequently, eyes for those likely to be more permanent. There are also several types of end-to-end connectors for splicing wires together.

Crimping tools all perform basically the same function, but vary slightly in design. Most types cut and strip wire ends in preparation for attaching connectors. In addition to crimping notches for standard wire sizes, some incorporate an extra-large notch for fastening connectors onto heavy auto-ignition cable. If you do a lot of car work, this is a good feature to look for. The better models also have bolt-cutting blades that will shear a bolt to exact length—a welcome aid if you need a non-standard size.

Recommended crimping techniques vary slightly so follow the instructions that come with the particular tool you buy. Some call for a single crimp; others advise a double crimp—one around the bare wire end and a second around the insulating sleeve.

Soldering wires

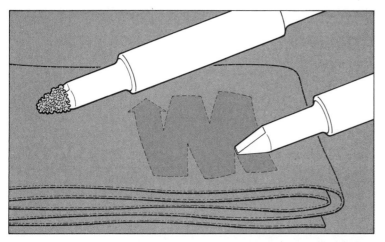

Keep your iron clean

A dirty iron won't transfer its heat to the joint efficiently. For best results, "tin" your iron's tip with a thin, shiny coating of solder before using it. After every few joints, clean the tip with a damp cloth or sponge—more often, if it acquires a dirty, dark or charred look, like the one shown at the far left. After cleaning, if the tip has lost its shiny appearance, re-tin it with another thin coat of solder. When the job is finished, clean and re-tin your iron again before you put it away

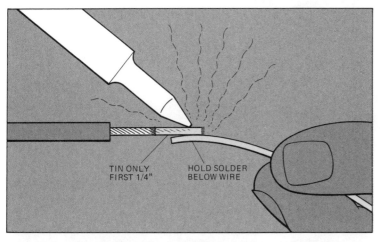

TIN ONLY FIRST 1/4"

HOLD SOLDER BELOW WIRE

Tin wires carefully

Tinning any wire with a thin coat of solder makes it easier to solder to a joint. Tinning standard wires also helps hold the strands together at the tip. Hold the solder below the wire so it will soak in, not drip on, and remove it and the iron once the solder has soaked into the first ¼ inch of the wire. Don't tin the remaining wire—it could become brittle and the joint could break if wires are flexed or pulled. When soldering shielded cable, be careful not to melt the insulation by applying too much heat

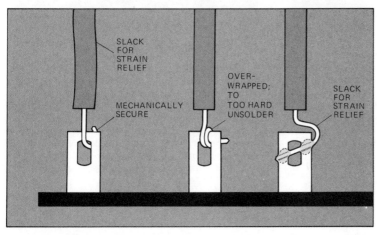

SLACK FOR STRAIN RELIEF

MECHANICALLY SECURE

OVER-WRAPPED; TO TOO HARD UNSOLDER

SLACK FOR STRAIN RELIEF

Make solid connections

Before soldering, wires should be bent to form mechanically secure connections (far left) that can stay in place even without solder; the solder's job is to maintain good electrical contact, not to glue wires in place. Leave some slack in the wire too, to prevent strain on the connection. Too complex a wrap (center) makes it harder to unsolder the wire for servicing. But a solder-only connection, with no wrapping, will usually yield a "cold-solder" joint

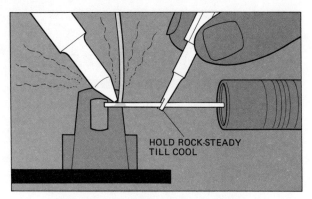

Keep wires stationary while cooling

Wires that move while the solder cools cause unreliable "cold-solder" joints. If you can't hold the wires in place with a good mechanical connection (as shown above, where a component lead is too short), hold them in place with soldering aids or other tools until the joint is cool. Brace your hands if necessary, to prevent shaking. Don't try to hold wires in place with the soldering iron—they'll spring up again as soon as you take the iron away. Soldering aids, of metal that solder doesn't stick to, also have many other uses

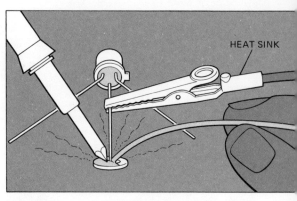

Heat sinks protect transistors

The heat of soldering can cook transistors and integrated circuits. If you're not using sockets, clip a heat sink between the joint and the transistor body to prevent this. Commercially made heat sinks are good, but you can also make your own from an alligator clip with a stub of heavy copper wire attached; or cement some felt into the clip's jaws and moisten it before each use. With no heat sink, use the least-powerful iron that will bring the joint quickly to soldering temperature. Too-small irons will cook more transistors than you'd think

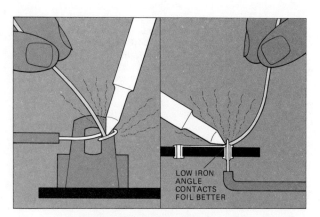

Heat the joint first, then solder

Don't just melt the solder and drip it onto the joint. First, heat the joint with the iron for a few seconds, then move the solder into contact with both the iron tip and all the parts or wires to be soldered. When the joint is hot enough, the solder will flow over and into it, wetting it evenly, filling in spaces, and cooling to a smooth, silvery sheen. If the joint takes more than three or four seconds to heat, though, you're using too small an iron for that job

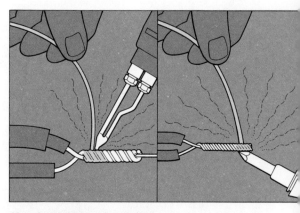

Use the right iron for the job

Electronic soldering is usually done best with medium-wattage pencil irons—hot enough to heat fine electronic wires quickly without cooking components. Heavy household wiring jobs are best done with high-wattage guns, powerful enough to heat the joint rapidly without having to bake wires and insulation for minutes; guns, which cool off between joints, are also handier than continuous-heating irons in the awkward places typical of house-wiring and other electrical situations

How to tell good solder joints from bad ones

Good solder joints (A) are smooth and shiny, with the outlines of all wires and contacts clearly visible, but with rounded fillets of solder filling in the gaps and corners where wires meet. Insufficient solder (B) leaves no fillets and may not maintain a reliable connection. Too much solder (C) covers a connection with big blobs (which sometimes cause short-circuit bridges between conductors on circuit boards); there may be a good joint underneath, but you can't see it to tell. Overheating (D) chars wire insulation and may lift solder pads from circuit boards or harm delicate components. Cold solder joints may have a jagged, crystalline look (E), a dripped-on, blobby appearance not conformant to outlines of the joint (F), or merely a hazy, milky sheen (not shown)

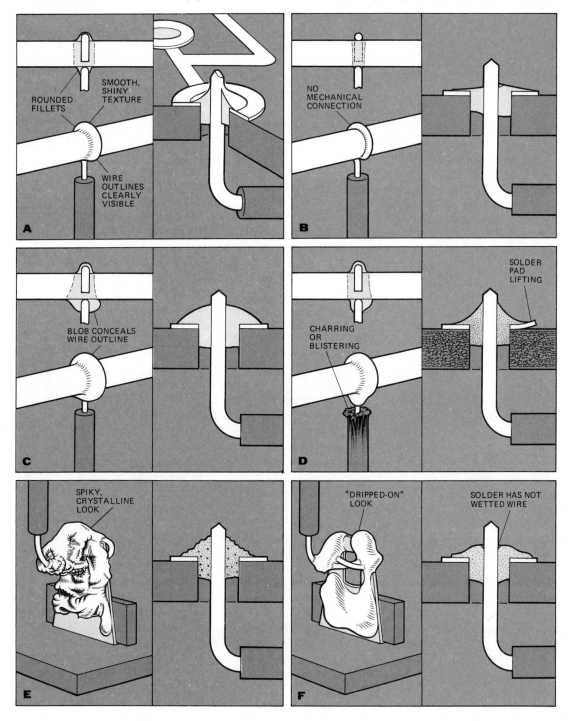

Doorbell repairs

■ THOUGH A DOORBELL setup is one of the easiest-to-understand mechanical systems in a typical home, a malfunctioning system is often neglected because the average home handyman thinks the service job is beyond his skills. The fact is a do-it-yourselfer easily can determine and correct a faulty system. But you do need an understanding of the basics of a doorbell system and some rather common "tools." The "tools" consist of common household articles like lighter fluid, cotton swabs and fine-grit sandpaper, plus a pocket continuity tester.

You should be aware that there is a difference between a line tester (for 110-v. branch-circuit testing) and a continuity tester. Both testers light up to show whether the part (or system) is working—*but a continuity tester is for low amperage only.* And it must be used with electric current off. Continuity testers can be purchased at hardware and electrical-supply stores.

The photo below shows the three doorbell components: door button, transformer and chime box. The step-down transformer lowers the household current from 115 v. to a doorbell working voltage of approximately 16 v.—enough to produce a strong magnetic field in the chime box terminal block when the circuit is completed by the doorbell button. A chime box is designed

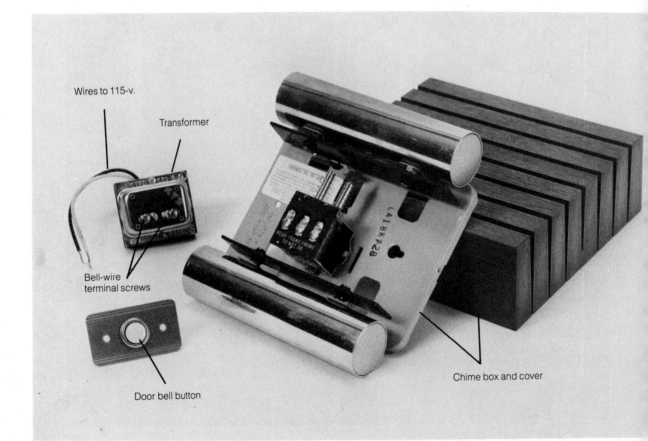

Wires to 115-v.

Transformer

Bell-wire terminal screws

Door bell button

Chime box and cover

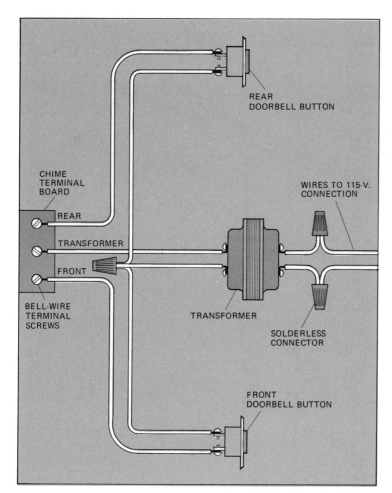

REAR
DOORBELL BUTTON

CHIME
TERMINAL
BOARD

REAR

TRANSFORMER

FRONT

BELL-WIRE
TERMINAL
SCREWS

WIRES TO 115-V.
CONNECTION

TRANSFORMER

SOLDERLESS
CONNECTOR

FRONT
DOORBELL BUTTON

BUZZERS and doorbells require low-voltage electricity through a transformer hookup. The transformer reduces the 115-v. current to voltage desired. In system at left, front and back door-chime hookup is accomplished by connecting wires as shown. Caution: Make certain that power is off when wiring the transformer to a 115-v.

BASIC COMPONENTS of doorbell/chime system are easier to understand than most homeowners suspect.

THREE SCREWS on chime-box terminal are easily accessible for making connections. The vertical plungers marked A, directly above the terminal screw board, should *never be oiled.*

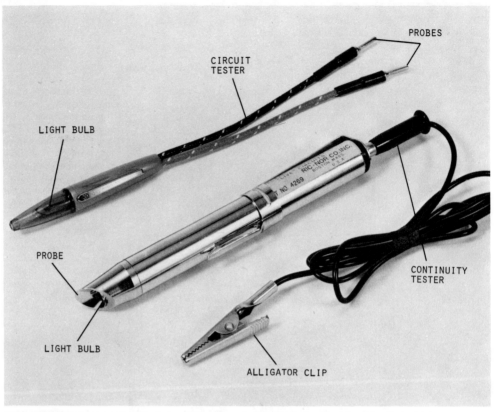

TWO TESTERS that you should always have in your toolbox are circuit and continuity testers. Whenever using the continuity tester *be sure* that the power is turned off.

for various tones: chimes, buzzing or ringing, depending on the model.

When the doorbell button is pressed, a circuit is completed at the chime-box terminal board. For example, if the front doorbell button is pressed, there will exist a voltage of 16 v. across the terminals marked *Trans.* and *Front.* This voltage creates a magnetic field in this terminal box which pulls a striker rod through its internal hole, causing it to hit one of the sound bars and produce the sound (something like a "ding"). When the button is released, the circuit is broken, the magnetic field at the terminal board collapses and the spring tension on the striker rod snaps the rod to the other sound bar producing a "dong."

Testing sequence for the system doesn't matter: Most often, however, the problem will be in either the chime box or doorbell button. Remove

the cover from the chime box and disconnect the three wires on the terminal board. Remove the two screws holding the electromagnet to the box and carefully lift out the terminal box, striker rods and springs. With a paper clip or nail file, pick the spring off of the striker rod, being extra careful not to stretch or deform it. Using cotton swabs soaked with lighter fluid, thoroughly clean the striker rods and striker-rod holes in the terminal block until they begin to shine. Reassemble springs on striker rods.

A very quick test can now be made of the chime-box terminal board to determine if the windings in each striker-rod hole are intact. Place the tester clip on the terminal marked *Trans.* and the continuity tester probe on either *Front* or *Rear* terminal. If the windings are good, the tester will light. Check both front and rear terminals in this manner. If the tester does not

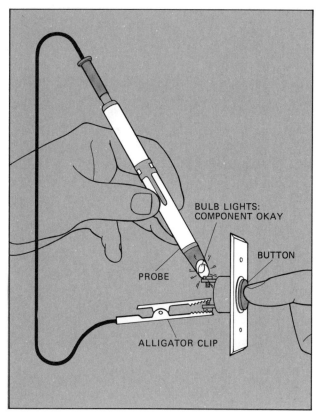

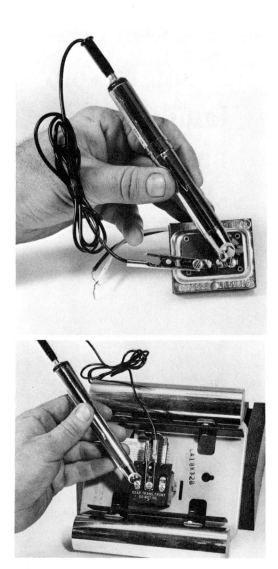

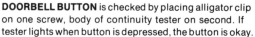

DOORBELL BUTTON is checked by placing alligator clip on one screw, body of continuity tester on second. If tester lights when button is depressed, the button is okay.

TRANSFORMER is checked for continuity by placing alligator clip on one screw, tester probe on the second.

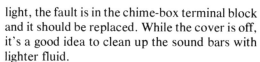

TO CHECK chime box, alligator clip is placed on center screw; front and rear-door terminals are then tested.

light, the fault is in the chime-box terminal block and it should be replaced. While the cover is off, it's a good idea to clean up the sound bars with lighter fluid.

To test the doorbell button, remove the two wires connected to the button. Place the continuity tester probe on one screw terminal and the clip on the other. Press the button to close the circuit. If the button is good, the tester will light. A spring(s)-loaded button (the type shown in the photos) cannot be repaired and must be replaced. A copper-strip button (usually rectangular in shape) *can* be repaired. To do it, first disassemble the button. Then, clean the copper contacts with fine sandpaper; also clean the copper in the terminal block of the button. Reassemble and test again. If it still doesn't work, replace it.

Before installing any new or repaired button, clean the bell wire (coming from the hole in the wall).

The last component to check is the transformer. *Caution: At your house service panel, first turn off the power to the transformer.* Next, place the continuity tester probe on one terminal screw and the clip on the other. If the transformer is good, the tester will light. A transformer that tests bad *must be replaced*.

The complete wiring diagram of a two-bell system is shown. If rewiring is necessary, use this as a guide. You are well advised to take the time to read through installation instructions to assure you completely understand them. Although some chime-box mechanisms may differ slightly from the model shown, the test procedures and the repairs will remain the same.

Protect your family from outdoor electric shock

■ ON A WARM Saturday morning, your kids head for your back-yard pool. About noon your wife decides to edge-trim the lawn with an electric edger. Later, you're cutting lumber with your portable circular saw (while standing on damp grass).

These are typical family activities on a weekend—yet three times different members of your family were exposed to the risk of serious electrical-shock injury and possible electrocution.

All it would take would be an insulation failure on a pool outlet, the edge trimmer or the electric surfaces that the tool user may contact. In short, those high-accident areas mentioned previously.

Total in-home protection is achieved by replacement of all circuit breakers with GFCI breakers. But the installation costs—even on a do-it-yourself basis—will escalate rapidly.

For indoor high-accident areas, consider replacing receptacles with a GFCI built into a duplex receptacle. One version is offered in two models (both intended for 15-amp., 120-v. circuits). One type provides individual outlet protection (dead-end); for a couple of dollars more, you can buy a feed-through version that will protect the entire circuit when it's installed on the first outlet of the branch line.

Or you can choose a portable type, which you can keep in your toolbox so it will be handy anywhere, indoors or out, when you have occasion to use any 110-v. power tool.

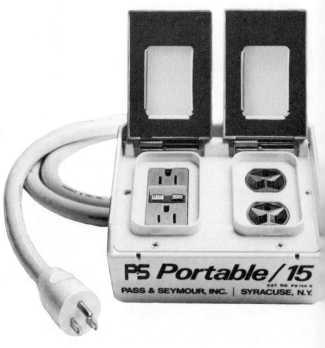

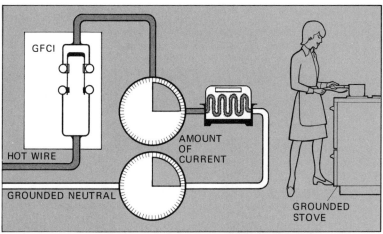

How ground-fault interrupter 'guards' circuit

SIMPLIFIED DRAWINGS at left show how a ground-fault circuit interrupter monitors current flow to assure equal current in the wires. Condition shown here is safe.

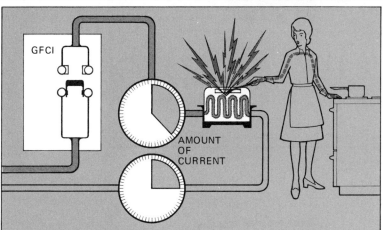

A GROUND FAULT changes current in one wire. Here, housewife wrongly poking a metal object into toaster creates a shock hazard—because she is "grounded" by touching a grounded metal stove. Upon sensing current difference, GFCI acts fast (trips) to shut off current.

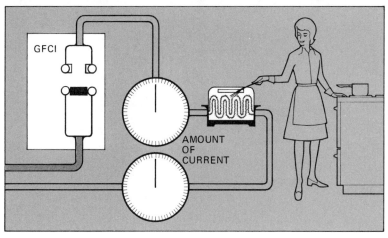

GFCI cuts off the circuit completely to eliminate the shock hazard just 25/1000ths of a second after it senses a ground fault. Thus, the circuit interrupter is, in effect, a circuit "watchdog."

A BRANCH CIRCUIT is completely protected when the breaker in the service panel is a GFCI type. Breaker (far left) takes up the same space as the circuit breaker it replaces. This manufacturer has models available for 15, 20, 25 and 30-amp. breakers.

CIRCUIT BREAKER (near left) by General Electric has 5-milliamp. ground-fault protection. It can be used to replace standard plug-on or bolt-on breakers. Available in 15, 20, 25 or 30 amps., 120-v., it has a 10,000-amp. interrupting capacity and a push-to-test feature to provide verification of performance.

Other types of interrupters

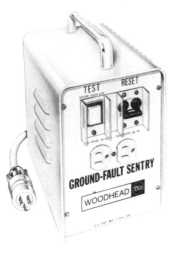  

THIS PORTABLE interrupter is designed for on-the-job ground-fault protection. The unit is simply plugged into a power source, and tools plug into it. Model is claimed to be the most sensitive GFCI available. It trips on 0.2 ma. of current.

A LOW-PRICED interrupter is built into a duplex receptacle and fits a standard outlet box. It's available in two models— dead-end protecting its own outlets, and feedthrough for protecting all outlets on the circuit.

THIS PORTABLE GFCI can plug into any 15-amp., 120-v. standard grounded receptacle to provide ground-fault protection; thus it is ideal to keep in your toolbox for use with power tools indoors or out.

Tin-can reel for an extension cord

■ HERE'S A PROJECT you can finish in an evening—an extension-cord reel that plays out as much line as you need, when you need it. Mounted on a swivel bearing, the cord unwinds quickly; when you're through with it, you merely crank it up.

It goes together quickly. Use two small screws through predrilled $\frac{3}{16}$-in. holes to attach the utility box to the plywood disc. Run the cord through two Romex connectors, one installed on the side of the can and the other in a knockout of the utility box. Leave about 8 in. of cord protruding from the box, then mount it using two round-head screws in the drilled holes. The disc with a rectangular cutout can now be installed with screws. Mount the swivel bearing on the upright first, then to the reel. To maintain polarity, wire the outlet as shown in the drawing.

TWO-LB. COFFEE can is the reel core.

THE CORD REEL can be assembled in one evening for pennies—the electric box and duplex will probably be your only expenses. When a job is finished, the cord is quickly cranked into the reel.

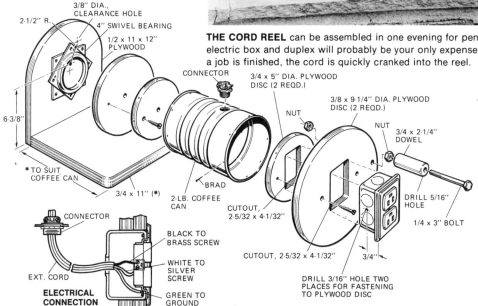

Evolution of today's electronics

■ OUR WORLD IS so dependent on electronic devices that it's hard to imagine life without them. Look around your home. Radio, TV, stereo, the microwave oven, telephone micro-computer, video games, typewriters, even coffee makers are all electronic intrusions into our lives. And don't forget the electronic ignition in your car.

Electronic vs. electrical

Electronic devices do depend on electric energy, but not every machine that consumes power is electronic. The word *electricity* itself describes the energy created by the movement of electrons.

Electrical devices convert electricity into mechanical action or heat. The simple motor on an electric fan—and even a light bulb—are more properly labeled as electrical.

The word *electronics* is reserved for devices in which the energy is precisely controlled. Vacuum tubes, diodes, transistors or integrated circuits are electronic components in such devices as a radio, TV, or car's electronic ignition.

Electronic theory

To understand modern electronics, you must begin with the basic concepts of electricity itself. These concepts are rooted in the behavior of electrons. What are electrons? Why do they move? How can we control the movement of electrons? If you can pass this short quiz, you probably are literate about today's technology. You also know, then, that the evolution of today's electronics centers on ways to give more reliable and precise control over the movement of electrons.

What are electrons?

Atomic structure. Everything is basically electrical. Matter consists of extremely small units called *atoms*. Each atom contains a certain number of paired particles of unequal size and opposite electrical charge. The larger, positively charged particles are called *protons*. They are in the nucleus, or center, of the atom's structure. The smaller, negatively charged particles are called *electrons*. They orbit around the nucleus, somewhat like the earth and other planets orbit around the sun. (Scientists have discovered that atoms also contain other particles and energy sources like neutrons. But they have little to do with electrical energy itself, so we'll leave them alone.)

Electrons not only twirl around their own atom's nucleus, they can be coaxed into moving to other atoms, sometimes harmoniously blending with their new neighbors, other times rudely evicting another electron and forcing it to find someplace else to go.

Why do electrons move?

Molecular structure. Everything is made up of *molecules.* That's the smallest particle into which something can be divided and still be recognized as part of that substance. Two or more atoms will combine into *elements* we know as copper, gold or oxygen. (Two or more of these elements can combine into *compounds* we know as wood, air or water.)

We can recognize a molecule of gold as different from a molecule of lead because of its molecular structure—the fixed number of energy pairs of electrons and protons in its atoms.

Electrical charge. In all molecules, the electrons and protons in the atoms tend to maintain a definite relationship because their opposite negative and positive charges attract each other. And they tend to remain in balance with the negative charges of the electrons exactly equal to the positive charge of the protons. Even so, there are conditions under which an atom in a molecule will lose some of its electrons to another atom, at least temporarily. When this happens, the atom with the extra electrons becomes negatively charged; the one that lost the electron displays the positive charge of its proton. Atoms that have lost or gained electrons are called *ions*.

Sketch and schematic diagram of Fleming's Electron Valve

Heated filament

Glass envelope

Connecting wires

Electron flow

Load resistor

Filament battery

Plate battery

Sketch and schematic of solid state diode

Glase sleeve

Wire wisker

Semiconductor element

DIODES ARE simple electronic devices with only two electrodes—a negative cathode and a positive anode. Current can be made to flow between them. In the solid-state diode, the negative element is often called the emitter and the positive is called the collector. Diodes are useful in rectifying alternating current (AC) into direct current (DC).

Free electrons and conductors. The electrons in molecules of some substances, like copper and other metallic elements, are not held very tightly to their protons and tend to wander freely from atom to atom. Since the free electrons in these elements can be made to move easily, the substances are called a *conductors*. Copper wire and silver contacts on switches are good conductors of electricity.

Bound electrons and insulators. In certain other elements, the electrons are tightly bound to their paired protons in the nucleus. Since these atoms don't give up electrons easily, movement of electrons between molecules doesn't happen as readily. These *nonconductors* or *insulators* are just as important to electrical circuits. Paper, glass and rubber are compounds made up of nonconducting elements we use as insulators in electrical circuits.

Fickle electrons and semiconductors. Some elements are made up of atoms so close to the delicate balance of paired charges that they will act as good conductors under some conditions and as insulators under other conditions. The changeable—but predictable—behavior of these *semiconductors* has played an important role in modern electronic devices such as transistors and microprocessors. Silicon is the most famous of these semiconductor elements.

Potential for electron movement. Electrons are law-abiding and would rather be in a harmonious balance with their protons instead of moving freely about. When the atoms in one molecule collect an excess of electrons the molecule has a negative charge. These electrons will immediately seek out an atom that needs them—one with a positive charge. If there is no place for these excess electrons to go, they collect and have the potential for movement once given the chance. The potential of these excess electrons is known as *voltage*.

Actual electron movement. *Current* is the movement of these electrons from a place where there is a negative potential because of an excess to a place where there is a more positive potential with fewer electrons. Electrical circuits provide a path for current flow with wires and the electronic components themselves.

How can we control the movement of electrons?

An understanding of technology focuses on an understanding of ways we have invented or discovered to control this movement: to get it to happen only when we want, in only the amount we want and only to where we want. The evolution of today's electronics begins with vacuum tubes and ends with microprocessors and smart-power chips.

Vacuum tubes

Operating principle. If you enclosed a piece of metal heated by a filament in a vacuumed tube (or one filled with an inert gas), you could have a fair number of free electrons bouncing around with nowhere to go until the growing positive charge on the metal they left pulled them back. But what if you also arranged a positively charged metal plate at the opposite end of the same tube? The freed electrons would tend to move straight toward the plate if it offered them a higher potential place to go.

If you varied the level of the positive charge on the plate, you would be able to determine when it

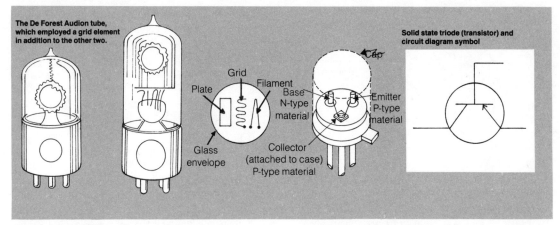

The De Forest Audion tube, which employed a grid element in addition to the other two.

Grid
Plate
Filament
Glass envelope

Base
N-type material
Collector (attached to case)
P-type material
Emitter
P-type material
Cap

Solid state triode (transistor) and circuit diagram symbol

TRIODE DEVICES have three electrodes and are often used to amplify currents passing through. In the tube form, a grid positioned between the cathode and the anode controls the rate of amplification by con-trolling the flow of electrons to the anode. In a solid-state device, a semiconductor layer called the plate, sandwiched between the emitter and the collector, is used in much the same way.

attracts electrons and when it doesn't. This would control the flow of electrons through the plate to an attached output circuit as if the tube were an on-off valve in sort of an "electrical pipe." (The British actually call a vacuum tube a valve.)

Diodes. The first vacuum tubes contrived in scientific laboratories in the last quarter of the nineteenth century were this simple. They were called *diodes* because they contained two charged *electrodes* inside. They permitted the thermionically emitted electrons to flow from a heated negatively charged *cathode* toward a positively charged plate called an *anode*.

At first their purpose was for the laboratory study of basic electricity and atomic structure. No one seemed concerned with practical applications of the tube. Thomas Edison developed such a device but later let its patent lapse.

Rectifiers. The chief virtue of the simple diode tube was its special ability to *rectify* alternating current (AC) into direct current (DC). DC travels in only one direction. One wire in a DC circuit is always positive, the other always negative. AC charges its direction in rapid cycles, usually around 60 per second. The wire that was positive during the first half of a cycle is negative in the second half. Many electrical devices can operate only from DC. Yet for a variety of quite practical reasons, most electric power is distributed in the form of wire-borne AC.

Rectification happens this way. AC electricity enters the diode in its customary cycles. The charge placed on the two electrodes is rapidly alternated between positive and negative. Electrons released from the heated cathode will travel to the anode plate only when the plate has a positive potential. This means the electrons flow in more or less continuous pulsations. Each pulsation represents only the positive half of the whole AC cycle. The negative half is lost because it failed to attract electrons to the plate. The pulsating current fed out of a rectifying tube is useful as one-way DC, although other processes are sometimes used to smooth out the pulses a bit.

Amplifiers. The original diode developed by the English scientist John Fleming in 1904 was not useful in power amplification. The simple kind of valve that the diode provided did little more than turn currents on and off. There wasn't much quantity control available.

It remained for the American inventor Lee De Forest to come up with an electronic device that would solve the amplification problem. In 1907 he perfected a tube called the *triode,* or *audion.* It added a third electrode to the valving process in the form of a tiny metal *grid.* The negatively charged grid was positioned directly between the cathode and the anode plate. By varying the negative charge on the grid, the flow of electrons between the heated cathode and the high-potential plate could be precisely controlled.

Since there was a separate source of electrons between the cathode and the anode, a relatively small negative charge on the grid could control a quite massive electronic flow to the triode's output circuit. The stronger the incoming signal, the more negative the grid. The more negative the grid, the weaker the electronic current through the plate. The resulting current output would reproduce the original waveform but with greater amplitude.

If you've been alert, you'll be quick to note that the output of this device was reversed from the controlling input signal. A strong input resulted in a weak output. It remained only to chain two triodes together to restore the signal to its original waveform relationship.

Electronic amplification is important to broadcast reception at two stages in the process. The incoming signals can be converted by a diode into usable DC, and the DC voltages can be magnified in stages to reproduce sounds (or images) of appropriate intensities.

Special vacuum tubes. Over the years, many different kinds of vacuum tubes have been developed for many purposes. One of these is the *electron beam*. Inside these devices, an electron gun aims a beam of electrons at an anode with holes in it just behind a luminescent surface. When the beam passes through a hole, the luminescent surface lightens up or darkens in response to the beam's electrical force. Magnetic or electromagnetic fields placed around the beam serve as an electronic lens system to direct and focus it at each of the anode holes in sequence. You probably know this special tube by a more common name, the TV picture tube. This is only one category of electron beams. Others are electron microscopes, X-ray tubes and oscilloscope displays.

Another type of exotic tube used to oscillate radar transmissions, the *magnetron,* was also found by accident to offer some very commendable culinary properties. Engineers testing these specialized diodes discovered that the microwaves they radiated tended to melt chocolate bars kept nearby. Some quick experiments led to their being designed into the now familiar microwave ovens found in so many restaurants and homes.

Photoelectric cells are tubes used to detect color, sort objects and react to "beam-breaking." Best known as *electric eyes,* these specialized vacuum tubes are designed so light can activate the cathode, sending current forward to the anode.

The vacuum tube legacy. Experiments with vacuum tubes have laid the groundwork for all modern electronics. They are so frequently used as an obsolete benchmark to describe what is happening in transistors and integrated circuits that we sometimes forget that they made voice transmission possible, moving us from the wire-bound telegraph into the age of radio and television. But they were big; they were hot; and they were usually unreliable. It took the ENIAC computer with its 18,000 heat-producing tubes filling two huge rooms to convince engineers and scientists they needed something better to control electron movement—something smaller, cooler, faster and more reliable.

Transistors

Transistors came into being in 1947 as a result of work done by three Americans: John Bardeen, Walter Brattain and William Shockley. While transistors perform the same kinds of electronic tasks associated with tubes, they do so by different methods.

Operating principles. Transistors are built of semiconductors like silicon and germanium. In nature, such materials lack the free electrons available with metals or certain highly conductive fluids and gases. They would never work to create current in electron tubes. But these semiconductors can acquire useful levels of free electrons through the painstakingly careful addition of certain chemical impurities to their otherwise pure crystalline structure. The process is called *doping.*

Semiconductors with a negative potential (N-type) get their free electrons from such impurities as phosphorus, antimony or arsenic. Impurities like boron, aluminum and gallium cause some electrons to be pulled away from the atoms of the semiconductor material, giving it a positive potential (P-type). This lack of an electron in an atom is called a *hole.* Holes can actually pass from one atom to another to produce current in a direction opposite from the movement of electrons.

Solid-state diodes. When a layer of N-type semiconductor material is placed with a layer of P-type material, we have a solid-state *diode.* These diodes, like their vacuum tube counterparts, pass current in only one direction and are used to either block current flow in one direction or to rectify the AC cycles into a steady DC current. You'll find pairs of these diodes rectifying the output of your car's alternator.

Transistors. A third layer of semiconductor material gives the diode characteristics of De Forest's triode tube. In these *transistor* devices, the terms *emitter, collector,* and *base* are used in place of the cathode, anode and grid of the vacuum tube, although their functions are not altogether dissimilar. The emitter and collector are separated by an opposing base type to which a small controlling voltage is applied to govern the larger current passing between them.

In many applications, transistors are used as electronic switches. A very small base current will turn on or off a much larger current between the emitter and collector. The point at which maximum current is allowed between the emitter and collector does not happen instantaneously, but gradually builds as the current of the base gradually gets stronger. The point at which the amount of base current allows maximum emitter-collector current to flow is called *saturation*. But when the base current varies just below the level of saturation, amplification takes place.

In amplifying circuits, you'll find transistors in your pocket radios and many circuits of your TV and similar appliances. In switching circuits, the transistor (with no moving parts of its own) has replaced the breaker points in automobile ignition systems. In 1954 Bell Labs built about 800 of these switching devices into the first transistorized computer, the TRADIC. The size of the computer was dramatically reduced, but not yet ready to put on your desk.

Integrated circuits

Designers began to develop circuits that used more than just one semiconductor, with diodes and transistors connected to each other on a printed circuit board. It was soon discovered that it was possible to put more than one transistor or diode on a silicon chip. This was known as *integrated circuits* (*IC*). From this start of putting just a few transistors and diodes on a chip, there has

THIS TINY integrated circuit chip holds thousands of transistors and diodes linked by complex photo-etched circuits. The chip is made of a pure semiconductor like silicon to which precise amounts of impurities have been added in order to unleash free electrons.

been a steady progress in the technology to where there are now chips with over 100,000 diodes, transistors and related circuits and components on an element smaller than a match head. These are now referred to as *large–scale integration* (*LSI*).

The results of these chips are evident in electronic calculators and games, watches and similar small devices. In 1964 IBM announced the System/360 that for the first time used LSI technology with components stored on integrated chips rather than discrete components such as transistors, diodes, resistors and coils on a circuit board. The company claimed these chips would last through 33 million hours of operation. Less than two decades earlier, the future of computers was dimmed by skeptics who pointed out that vacuum tube failure occurred every 15 minutes!

Microprocessors

In 1969 Dr. Ted Hoff got the idea of putting the arithmetic and logic circuits of a pocket calculator on a single chip of silicon instead of connecting a number of special function chips together with circuitry. This *central processing unit* (*CPU*), developed on a chip smaller than a fingernail, almost matched the power of the ENIAC with its 18,000 vacuum tubes. This CPU is combined with other chips to provide for memory storage and control functions, but the basic electronics are still on a printed circuit board less than one foot square. The microcomputer was ready for the desktop—and lap!

Microprocessors are not only found in home computers. They are now commonplace in cars, controlling everything from ignition and fuel injection to brakes and windshield washers. There's even an accessory on the market today that will locate the position of your car on a map of the area you are in displayed on a small TV screen in your car. By entering where you want to go, the device will plot out the best route to take to get there, even to the extent of sensing traffic information from other computer systems and giving you a route that will avoid traffic jams.

More recent developments

Microprocessors do not represent the only important recent developments in modern electronics. *Lasers* and the *smart-power chip* also have brought us new possibilities.

Lasers. A laser uses concentrated light rays as an extremely broad bandwidth in which to transmit or read communication signals. *Bandwidth* refers to the width of the band of frequencies needed to transmit electronic information from one place to another. Two things can occupy bandwidth: the amount of information needed to transmit an electronic image or other signal; and the number of these signals that can be sent over the same communications link. The wider the bandwidth, the more signals with more information can be sent. The laser's name was formed from its own definition: **l**ight **a**mplification by **s**timulated **e**mission of **r**adiation. Lasers can be used to create holograms, pictures that are truly three-dimensional. They are also used daily to send an incredible number of telephone and data messages in a single light beam transmitted through the air or over special optical cables made of glass fibers.

One of the more interesting applications of low-powered lasers is found in *optical discs*. These shiny, grooveless recordings of various diameters can be used to hold holographically imprinted digital data. The laser beam scans the disc and picks up signals of enormous bandwidth that can be converted into video pictures, audio music or computer data of extraordinary fidelity. The smaller, one-sided form of the laser disc is called a *CD* (compressed disc) and is used mainly to store high-fidelity musical material. The larger, two-sided forms are commonly referred to as *videodiscs*. They can store conventional TV pictures as well as interactive video and computer data. One side of a videodisc no larger than an LP record can hold up to 54,000 different frames of information or pictures.

Smart-power chips. No electronic development in recent years holds out more promise than the *smart-power chip*. These little microprocessors can manage electrical flows like computer chips have been doing for some years now, but with an historic difference. The smart-power chip can deal with voltages as high as 100 times the 5 volts earlier chips could handle.

Where the transistor and integrated circuits replaced the electronic functions of the vacuum tube, smart-power chips are likely to replace the mechanical functions of gears and pulleys. They'll be able to control the energy consumption of ordinary electric motors in such things as electric drills and washing machines by matching their speed to the actual load encountered.

They'll be used in automobiles to amplify electrical systems and make them far more useful than they are now. These remarkable new electronic chips will make it possible to run a single loop of one or two tiny wires around the perimeter of your car to connect all the various lights and switches into one computer-controlled system. (Now each light or accessory has to have its

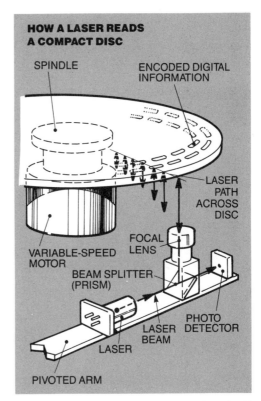

HOW A LASER READS A COMPACT DISC

SPINDLE
ENCODED DIGITAL INFORMATION
LASER PATH ACROSS DISC
VARIABLE-SPEED MOTOR
FOCAL LENS
BEAM SPLITTER (PRISM)
PHOTO DETECTOR
LASER BEAM
LASER
PIVOTED ARM

DIGITALLY RECORDED music is stored on the underside of a Compact Disc as microscopic pits etched into a perfectly reflective foil, laminated into the disc's transparent protective coating. The pits are arranged along a spiral, like a phonograph-record groove, but they start at the inside of the disc. The disc rotates slower when the laser moves toward the edge because the pits must pass the finely focused laser beam at a constant linear velocity. The laser beam is reflected up through a prism and focused onto the whirling disc's reflective layer. The beam, interrupted by the speeding pits, is reflected back down through the lens and prism, and is perceived by the photo detector as incredibly rapid on/off pulses.

wires ending up in a bulky and very heavy cable harness in which individual circuit wires are all but impossible to replace if they go, and which adds substantially to the weight—and cost—of the car.)

The smart-power chips will be widely used in home appliances, automobiles and factory settings by 1990. Lasers are already making headway in the marketplace. So what's next in electronics? The sky's the limit—literally. What would you say to appliances that pulled their electrical power "out of the air" instead of from a cord plugged into a wall socket? Maybe—someday. Technologists seem to have a way of coming up with the improbable pretty fast. The impossible takes a little longer.

Some electronic typewriters are computerlike. The IBM Model 95 accommodates a floppy-disk drive for added word storage, and a communications module to send documents to another unit over the phone.

Electronic typewriters

■ MOST OF US probably look upon typing as a chore—hardly a source of enjoyment or entertainment! But it's true—technology has made the latest generation of electronic typewriters absolutely fascinating to use. The combination of programmable memory and high-speed printing takes the most tedious burdens off the typist's hands, and the computerlike features of today's electronic typewriters enable the user to correct, revise and even rearrange a document with a minimum of retyping.

Electronic typewriters—ETs for short—aren't limited to busy corporate offices. They're widely available now in a broad range of models that offers varying degrees of sophistication. The simplest portable can help a student correct mistakes or perform minor revisions while typing a term paper. A more advanced, stationary model would have enough internal memory to store the entire assignment, allowing the student to restructure the piece, add footnotes or even new blocks of text to the paper. The most sophisticated ETs can be hooked up to an external memory-storage device as a computer floppy-disk drive. This means a student could record the entire content of a doctoral thesis (or even a novel) and make revisions electronically on a video monitor instead of on paper. When deadline approaches, pressing a button would send the final draft onto the paper at high speed.

Compared to conventional electric typewriters, the appearance of an ET is at once familiar and strange. Most ETs are wider than the electric and the manual typewriters from which they evolved—usually wide enough to accommodate computer paper 17 in. wide. The keyboard looks similar too, but you'll find banks of additional program keys on either side of the ET's alphanumeric keyboard. Lift the ET's lid, though, and you're in for a surprise.

In place of the familiar rods and levers, the ET substitutes a mass of circuit boards and a single, mobile printing unit. The latter is the only part you'll see: Most manufacturers conceal the circuit boards beneath the keyboard or behind the platen. One company boasts its machines have 30 moving parts, down from 300.

How it works

When you depress a character key, you activate a switch on a layer just below the keyboard.

This sends an electrical signal to the circuit board, which relays the signal to a microprocessor.

Up to this point, everything is quiet, invisible and instantaneous as the signal moves along wires or flat, ribbonlike cables to the printing unit. At the printing unit, the ET begins to sound off and show its mechanical dexterity.

Print wheels

On most ETs, the business end of the printing unit is a "daisy wheel" about 3 in. in diameter. The daisy is composed of typebars or "petals" with a letter, number or symbol at the tip of each. (Some machines use a golf-ball-like element for printing; the simpler portables use a dot-matrix mechanism.

In response to keyboarded instructions, the daisy wheel spins at high speed to position the selected petal before the ink ribbon. The daisy takes its directions from a stepper motor (see technical illustration). Once the petal is in position, it's struck by a plunger and hammer assembly. The petal, in turn, strikes the ink ribbon to make an impression of its character on the paper.

Character preview display

Most models will let you preview what you're composing through a visual display window similar to electronic calculators. You can then backspace, on the visual display, to correct your spelling or revise your text *before* you command the ET to print on paper.

The character capacity of the display window varies with the particular ET model. Portables show you a few words at a time, intermediate models an entire line, and the most sophisticated ETs display half a page or more at a glance.

Copy storage

Compared to the amount of copy you can see, the amount you can revise before printing depends on how much internal memory the machine offers.

With many inexpensive portables, you're usually limited to the character capacity of the display window. Most manufacturers' intermediate, stationary models can store between 10 and 20 pages in their internal memory. If you write lengthy documents, or if your work involves producing many versions of a similar document (a

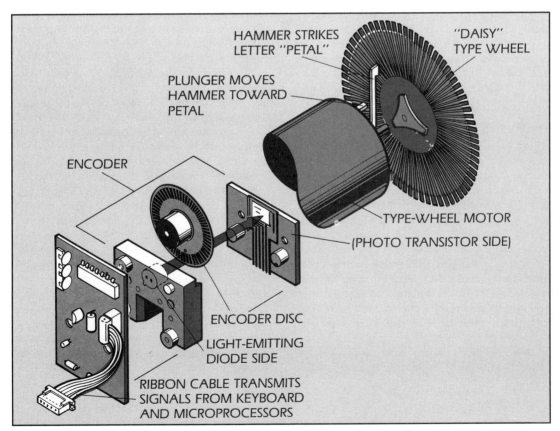

HAMMER STRIKES LETTER "PETAL"

"DAISY" TYPE WHEEL

PLUNGER MOVES HAMMER TOWARD PETAL

ENCODER

TYPE-WHEEL MOTOR

(PHOTO TRANSISTOR SIDE)

ENCODER DISC

LIGHT-EMITTING DIODE SIDE

RIBBON CABLE TRANSMITS SIGNALS FROM KEYBOARD AND MICROPROCESSORS

TYPICAL ET PRINTING unit: Encoder changes keyboard signal to light, tells motor to find the desired petal and to print.

right-hand margins to give the appearance of a printed page. With some ETs you don't even have to strike the carriage return at the end of the line, but your copy will automatically "wrap around" to the next line when your right margin is reached. This feature alone can speed up your typing time dramatically.

Some worthwhile functions involve pressing several program keys in sequence. For example, you might press the search and replace keys to make your ET find a word or phrase you wish to change. It will print out your text up to that point, then stop and wait for your orders. You simply add the new or revised text and press the insert key. What if you discover you've misspelled a word throughout your document? Simply program your ET to perform global search and replace, and it will locate and correct the mistake everywhere the word appears. Some ETs are so sophisticated they can transmit your finished copy to another ET. This is done over phone lines through the addition of an accessory telephone modem.

Computer features with typewriter ease

With disk drives, video display monitors and telephone modems, the somewhat understated ET begins to take on the appearance of a computer. It isn't. An ET won't perform accounting programs for you, nor will it let you play computer games. It doesn't tie into as many telephone-line data networks as computers do. A computer, though, will perform the word-processing chores an ET will.

So why not buy a computer? One reason is convenience. If all you're going to do is type, there's no point in mastering the complexities of a computer's word-processing program. Another reason is cost: With a computer, you'll be paying for functions you don't intend to use.

For those who already own computers for word-processing chores, the ET can be an inexpensive alternative to a letter-quality printer to supplement the higher-speed dot matrix printer you use for rough drafts. Most ETs can be modified to accept the output of your computer through the familiar printer ribbon cable connections without losing the advantages of having a sophisticated typewriter for tasks where the computer's storage or word-processing capabilities are not needed.

standard legal contract or form letter, for example), you might consider a more sophisticated ET—one that allows you to add external storage devices (floppy-disk drive or cassette recorder) with virtually unlimited memory. In this case, you'll probably want a video display monitor, too.

Special functions

One feature made possible by the ET's internal memory is the ability to store frequently used phrases. You can type a phrase (such as "payment due upon receipt") once and assign it to a particular program key in memory. When you come to the place in a letter where the phrase is needed, you simply press the key and the ET types your phrase for you.

Those program keys are capable of numerous automatic functions, depending again on the ET model. Besides the usual margin, tab, indent and backspace functions, the program keys can perform time-consuming tasks such as underlining each word as you type it and erasing one character at a time or an entire line at once. ETs can center titles in your document, or even justify

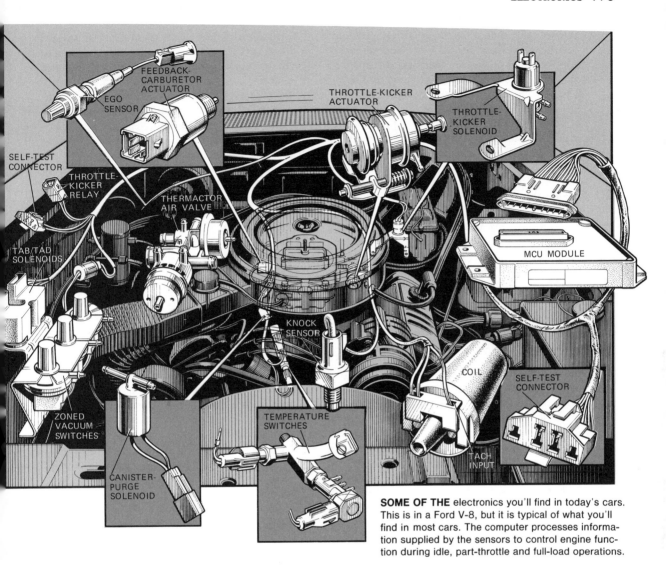

SOME OF THE electronics you'll find in today's cars. This is in a Ford V-8, but it is typical of what you'll find in most cars. The computer processes information supplied by the sensors to control engine function during idle, part-throttle and full-load operations.

Electronics in your car

■ ADVANCES IN microprocessor technology have brought about changes in the automotive electrical system. Circuit designers can now put a microprocessor, a small-size but very real computer, in the automobile to replace many of the mechanical devices once commonplace and to handle the emission-control jobs that mechanical parts never could do with the precision required.

All this complexity is found in the automotive electrical system for these reasons: (1) The cost is greatly reduced compared to the older electromechanical system; (2) solid-state components are now improved so they can work in the hostile environment of the heat under the hood.

Automotive microprocessors

The microprocessors now in cars are similar in operation to the computers used in homes and business. The microprocessor has to be *programmed;* it has to contain a set of instructions to tell it what to do. Normally, the circuit designer does this after the circuit is built on the silicon chip.

The microprocessor has many *inputs* from various points on the engine and transmission that sense and advise what's going on. These sensors monitor such things as outside air temperature, underhood temperature, engine coolant temperature, manifold pressure, exhaust gas oxygen content, vehicle speed, transmission range and more. The microprocessor constantly senses all these things, and because it has a *memory,* keeps track of them. Then its *central processing unit* (CPU) makes calculations based on all this information and comes up with answers to send back *output* telling other parts to control such things as the amount of fuel that should be metered into the engine, the best time to fire each spark plug and the best time for the transmission to shift. This all leads to an engine/transmission combination that can run at its most efficient level.

Development of electronic control systems

The change to electronics started slowly in the late 1960s with the replacement of relay-activated voltage regulators by fully electronic regulators, controlling voltage and current output of the alternator. Electronic ignition systems followed. Chrysler was first in 1973. Ford and GM made electronic ignition standard in 1974 and 1975. By 1980, virtually all cars, including imports, had electronic ignition. In 1976, Chrysler introduced the Electronic Lean Burn system. It adjusted ignition timing by use of a computer instead of the traditional mechanical and vacuum advances. In 1978, Ford introduced its first Electronic Engine Controls (EEC-1), the feedback carburetor, plus a miles-to-empty display. Ford continued its development of electronic controls in 1979 by producing a second-generation engine control, an electronic digital clock and an electronic cruise control with a "resume" feature based on an electronic memory.

General Motors was also expanding its use of electronics during these years. Starting with the compact High Engery Ignition (HEI) systems and the integral regulated alternator, GM went on to produce a version of the feedback carburetor, electronic fuel injection and electronic spark timing. It also provided a modified HEI system on its Seville that had a digital trip computer providing the driver with mpg, range, speed and estimated time of arrival.

The electronic control system

The electronic control system consists of three basic parts: (1) *sensors* to tell what is happening somewhere in the vehicle; (2) the *processor* to add up this information and decide what should be done about it; and (3) some *control* to change an operation.

Sensors. Small electronic devices at various locations throughout the car provide the input to the microprocessor. These devices can monitor changes in such things as temperature, speed, even the chemical makeup of exhaust gases. Sensors in a typical electronic system will monitor exhaust gas oxygen content, vehicle speed, manifold pressure, throttle position, coolant temperature and air conditioner operation.

Processor. Sensors send the computer *analog* signals—signals of varying nature such as different voltages indicating the rise and fall of temperature. The processor must first convert these analog signals into the *digital* on-off information the computer understands. It then is ready to make the split-second decisions and translate it back into analog information to control some operation.

Control. This output from the computer is then used to control a mechanical device such as a motor or solenoid that is attached to a component in the vehicle. Typically, the onboard computer will control fuel metering in the carburetor or fuel injection system, idle speed, distributor advance, transmission operation, exhaust gas recirculation valves or other emission-control devices, and driver conveniences and warnings such as a "Check Engine" light.

Operation. A typical electronic control system will continuously monitor each of the sensors and actuators for proper operation. It will alert the driver to a malfunction by means of a "Check Engine" light on the dash. It will substitute values of its own for critical sensors if they go bad to allow continued operation of the vehicle until it can be repaired. And it provides a trained service technician with a way to question the microprocessor to receive information in the form of a diagnostic code to isolate a malfunction.

The average do-it-yourselfer can feel overwhelmed by the electronics in a car today. Many trained service technicians shared this feeling not too many years ago. As car electronics become more routine, do-it-yourself checking and repair will also become more commonplace. Handheld electronic ignition testers, for example, are now sold in some auto supply stores for the do-it-yourselfer. It could be possible, however, to destroy a $400 control module with the voltage from the batteries in a voltmeter if the leads were even momentarily connected to the wrong terminals. Until you feel completely comfortable with electronics and the electronic systems in your car, it is best to proceed with caution or leave the job to trained professionals.

Build a 'brain' to test and recharge most batteries

BATTERY BRAIN clips are connected to the battery to be tested. If it needs charging, you plug in the battery eliminator or another power source at jack J1.

■ EVERYBODY KNOWS that batteries "give up" just when you need them most. You can prevent this frustrating annoyance with our Battery Brain. It has features not normally available on chargers, such as an adjustable charge rate. But particularly valuable are an automatic current cutoff that prevents a damaging overcharge and a light that lets you know your batteries are "ready."

Testing is a snap. All you do is flip a switch that corresponds to your battery voltage, touch the clips to the battery terminals, then watch the meter. If the meter needle moves, your battery has life. How much depends on how far the needle moves toward the 1.5 mark (0.9 means dead and 1.5 indicates a full charge).

If the needle doesn't move at all, throw out the battery.

How it works

Consider a single carbon-zinc or alkaline flashlight battery. Fresh from the store, it's rated at 1.5 v., but this falls steadily as the battery is used. The 1.5 and 0.9 on the Battery Brain meter scale represent the working voltage range of a single-cell, 1½-v. battery.

But say you want to test a more powerful 9-v. radio battery (composed of six 1½-v. cells in series). The Battery Brain simply divides all the voltages by six.

RECHARGE YOUR BATTERIES

Percent of energy remaining in carbon-zincs and alkalines for various voltages:

1.5 = 100%	
1.4 = 85%	
1.3 = 65%	
1.2 = 35%	
1.1 = 20%	
1.0 = 10%	
0.9 = 0%	

Recommended charge currents for different-size battery cells:

AAA	20 ma.
AA	40 ma.
C	60 ma.
D	100 ma.
9-v.	10 ma.
Lantern	140 ma.

PARTS LIST—BATTERY BRAIN

All resistors are ¼-w. carbon unless otherwise specified.

R1—1-ohm resistor
R2—100-ohm resistor
R3—200-ohm resistor
R4—300-ohm resistor
R5—390-ohm resistor
R6—510-ohm resistor
R7—680-ohm resistor
R8—4.7K (4700-ohm) resistor
R9—110-ohm resistor
R10—3.3K (3300-ohm) resistor
R11—10K (10,000-ohm) resistor
R12—10K (10,000-ohm) resistor
R13—100-ohm resistor
R14—10K (10,000-ohm) resistor
R15—1K adjustable trimmer control
R16—1K adjustable trimmer control
Q1—2N4403 PNP transistor (TO5 case)
Q2—2N4403 PNP transistor (TO5 case)
Q3—2N4403 PNP transistor (92 case)
Q4—2N4403 PNP transistor (92 case)
Q5—2N4401 NPN transistor (92 case)
D1, D2, D3—1N4148
M1—0-200uA edge meter
S1 = S8—8-position DIP switch
L1, L2—6-v., 70-ma. lamp
J1—Jack, open-circuit type
Misc.: Wire, clips for batteries, solder.

Charge! (and save)

Charging is as simple as testing with the Battery Brain. Once it is set up to test a battery, plugging a 9- to 15-v. source into the Battery Brain's jack automatically converts it into a charger.

Measures rising voltage

The meter still works, except that it now measures the rising voltage of the battery as it is charged. A light shows that you're charging and goes out when your battery is fully charged. If you want to charge a battery of different voltage, just flip the switch on the case to whatever new voltage is desired.

One of the best and most convenient sources for the 9- to 15-volts is one of the little modular, plug-in-the-wall battery eliminators. Since any 9- to 15-v. source will power the Battery Brain, you can also make an adapter that plugs into your car's 12-v. cigaret lighter.

When to recharge

Generally, it's best to recharge a battery when the voltage falls between 1.2 and 1.4. Normally, you can count on more than 10 recharges on such batteries as carbon-zincs, heavy-duties and alkalines. Nicads are even better; they're designed to be recharged repeatedly and can go more than 1000 cycles.

Just as falling voltage indicates the state of discharge, how far the voltage rises toward 1.5 v. indicates how much charge the battery has taken. You adjust the cutoff trimmer control so the charging lights go out *just* at 1.5 v. This way, the cutoff is set properly for all the different battery voltages you will use in charging.

Different charge currents

Different-size batteries need different charge currents. The chart shows the recommended rates for various batteries. You set the current level with the charge control and judge by the brightness of the lights: Dim red = 20 milliamperes (ma.); bright red = 30 ma.; orange = 50 ma.; yellow = 60 ma.; white = 70 ma. These values are doubled when you flip the "C" switch. So you get a charge current range of 20 ma. to 140 ma.

Construction

Construction is easy. You install and solder all the components on the drilled, etched and labeled printed-circuit (PC) board. If you prefer to make your own PC board, we supply a template.

Resistors R1 through R7 divide the different battery voltages down to 1.5. Which one is in the circuit is selected by one of seven switches. Before the meter gets the voltage, the "unwanted" 0.9 v. is subtracted out by diodes D2 and D3. The circuitry on the left shuts off the charge current (which flows through the lamps) when the voltage per cell of the battery you are charging reaches 1.5 v.

Note: In order for your battery to get a charge, the voltage of your source has to be higher than that of your battery. So if you are charging 9- or 12-v. batteries, you need at least a 12-v. or higher source.

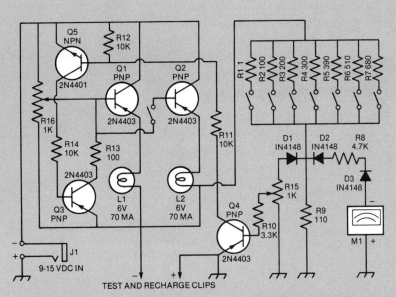

THE SCHEMATIC diagram (above) details how Battery Brain's components are interconnected.

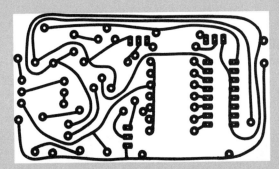

COMPONENT-SIDE view (below) shows how all the parts of the Battery Brain are to be placed on the printed-circuit board. You can easily make the PC board by using the template which is shown above.

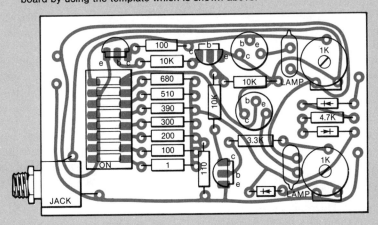

Power meter and stylus timer

THE POWER METER (right, above) will show just how many watts are getting to your speakers. The stylus timer (pictured atop the turntable) will meter out the hours your stylus has been tracking the grooves so that you will know when to replace it.

■ IF YOU HAVE an expensive stereo set, the most crucial and easily damaged components are the largest and the smallest—your speakers and your stylus. Here are two projects, a power meter and a stylus timer, that can be added to most stereo systems.

A power meter, even a three-range one like ours, is a very simple circuit. Essentially, it's a resistor, a diode and a meter in a series circuit. Its function is to measure the voltage going into the speakers. The more voltage, the more power the speakers use. The nonlinear meter scale converts this into the customary units of power—watts.

In the circuit, each resistor limits the voltage going into the sensitive meter and also determines the range of 1, 10 or 100 watts. Since there are three ranges, you need three resistors and a switch to select the desired range. The diode rectifies the a.c. voltage to the speakers into d.c. voltage that the meter can display.

But you need two independent meters, one for each stereo channel. The solution is to duplicate the circuit—so that you have six resistors, two diodes and one double-pole, double-throw switch.

In the construction, you solder these parts onto a printed-circuit board, along with the clips that will hold the speaker leads, or use point-to-point wiring. Using hookup wire, connect the M1+ pad

on the circuit board to the plus meter terminal. Likewise, the M1− pad goes to the minus meter terminal. This is repeated for the second meter, using the M2+ and M2− pads on the circuit board.

Next, glue the circuit board to the clear-plastic support rails. Set the board so you get a good view of it through the smoked plastic. Finally, connect the speaker wires to the circuit-board clips. One channel goes to the two clips on one side of the circuit board and the other channel goes to the other side.

Now you can test your system. On the 1-watt scale, even at very low volume, the meters will bounce in synchronization with the loudness. Of course, as you increase the volume, the deflection becomes greater.

You should switch over to the 10- or 100-watt range when the meter needles reach the end of the lower scale.

As you move up to the higher wattage scales, you may be surprised that the sound level you hear doesn't seem to increase nearly as fast as the meters indicate. In other words, 100 watts doesn't sound 10 times louder than 10 watts, but perhaps only twice as loud.

There's nothing wrong with the meters—your own ears' logarithmic response cuts down loud sounds and builds up soft ones. It's the only way

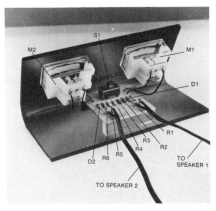

POWER METER contains two circuits that are mirror images of each other—one power-measuring circuit with two meters, one for each of your speakers.

STYLUS TIMER uses a unique mecury-plating device to measure the passage of time. When "used up," just reverse contacts and the meter is reusable.

THESE FOIL and component-side views show how to make the printed circuits for both projects. Alternatively, you can use the schematics above to do your own layout.

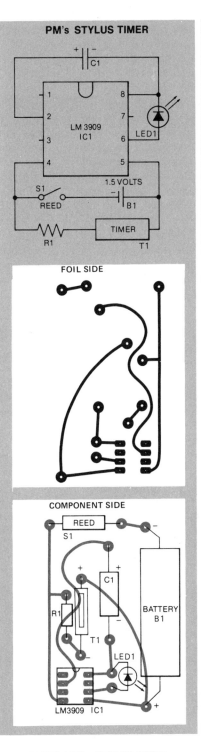

PM's STYLUS TIMER

LM 3909 IC1
LED1
1.5 VOLTS
S1 REED
B1
R1
TIMER
T1

FOIL SIDE

COMPONENT SIDE

REED
S1
C1
R1
BATTERY B1
T1
LED1
LM3909 IC1

PM's POWER METER

SPK1   SPK2
D1   D2
R4   R5
R3   R1   R2   R6
S1
M1   M2
SPK1   SPK2

SWT DPDT

FOIL SIDE

COMPONENT SIDE

M1 −   M1 +   D1
R1
R2
R3
DPDT S1
R4
R5
R6
SPK 1
SPK 2
M2 −   M2 +   D2

PARTS LIST—STYLUS TIMER

B1: AA-size battery, 1.5 v.
IC1: LM3909 LED flasher integrated circuit
LED1: Light-emitting diode
R1: 430K carbon resistor
S1: Reed switch
T1: Mercury tube timer (Curtis Instruments)
PCB: Drilled, etched and labeled printed-circuit board.
Misc.: Drilled and machined aluminum case, small bar magnet.

PARTS LIST—POWER METER

D1, D2: Germanium diodes (LN34A or equivalent)
M1, M2: Meter with power scale
R1, R6: 56K carbon resistors, 1/4 w.
R2, R3: 24K carbon resistors, 1/4 w.
R4, R5: 5.1K carbon resistors, 1/4 w.
S1: d.p.d t. slide switch
PCB: Drilled, etched and labeled printed-circuit board.
Misc.: Formed, machined, smoked Plexiglas holder, wire, solder, printed-circuit-board connection clips.

you can make sense of the range of sound levels you hear in a typical day—where the loudest can be a billion times stronger than the softest.

The stylus tip on your record player leads a very harsh life indeed. While being crushed by up to 33 tons of pressure per square inch, it's dragged over two-thirds of a mile of hard plastic per hour. If that's not enough, it's whipped from side to side in the groove with accelerations of more than 100 Gs, up to 20,000 times per second!

Even a diamond, the hardest substance in the world, can't hold up indefinitely under these conditions. The result—a chipped, raspy tip abrading two-thirds of a mile of your valuable record groove per hour—is certainly something you would like to avoid. Unfortunately, you can't stop the steady erosion of the tip, but if you keep track of playing time, you can insert a new tip before your record player turns into a record shredder.

And keeping track of time is just what the stylus timer does. As soon as your records start spinning, the timer's LED starts to flash, and the elapsed-time meter moves down its 0 to 1,000-hour scale.

Actually, nailing down the exact stylus playing time isn't quite as simple as it first appears. Where do you tap into your system so that the timer is activated only when records are being played? For example, the ON-OFF switch is "on" when the radio or tape deck is used—neither of which wears out styluses. Applying the same logic eliminates such tie-in points as speaker outputs, switched outlets, preamp outputs and so forth.

But every time you play a record, you move the play lever, and when the record is done, the lever snaps back on its own. So here is where the stylus timer records playing time with a magnetically activated reed switch. This way, you avoid the difficult task of "hard-wiring" into your system.

Inside the stylus timer case is an interesting combination of old and new technology. The flashing LED, which lets you know the stylus timer is "timing," is driven by a modern IC developed only a few years ago. This IC is so efficient, it can flash the LED for more than 3,000 hours on a single alkaline penlight cell.

The elapsed-time meter relies on the old and seemingly inappropriate technology of electroplating—plating one metal on another using electric current. During electroplating, the amount of metal which is plated is only a function of the current multiplied by the time the current is flowing. If you keep the current constant, then the plating becomes only a function of time, which is the variable we want to determine. But to determine the actual time, you have to determine the exact amount of metal plated—not an easy task.

Enter a clever idea—so clever, in fact, that it was patented recently. Instead of plating solid metals, why not use a liquid metal—mercury? Put it in a small-diameter glass tube with a liquid electrolyte "gap" in the mercury column.

When the current is passed through the tube, the mercury on one side is plated onto the mercury on the other side of the gap. As the mercury changes sides, so to speak, the gap travels down the tube. The elapsed time is shown by the location of the gap on the printed time scale next to the tube.

In the circuit—as you might expect—the tube current starts when the reed switch closes (play lever on). The 430K (430,000-ohm) resistor sets the current so the gap takes 1,000 hours to go down the scale. Different resistors give other scales.

And the stylus timer can be reused. When the gap reaches the end of the scale, you reset it to zero by reversing the tube holder.

The function of the LM3909 IC and the capacitor is to flash the LED. They are powered through the reed switch to give you a fail-safe indication that the timer is operating.

To use the stylus timer effectively, check how long the manufacturer recommends you should go between stylus changes. Typically, for diamond styluses, it's 800 hours.

But deviations from ideal playing conditions can cut this time considerably. Dirty records can knock 30 percent off the figure. Even more critical is the tracking force—the weight that holds the needle in the groove. The ideal force for good systems is around 1¼ grams. Up at 3 grams, stylus life can be cut in half. Too little tracking force, however, is worse than too much: An underweight stylus "chatters" and chews out the sides of the groove.

Electric outlet checker

THE TESTER measures line voltage and checks outlet wiring (see table below). Designed for three-wire grounded outlets, it can also check three-wire adapters used in two-wire outlets; here, light shows that the "ground" screw isn't really grounded

CONDITION	METER READING	LAMPS
PROPERLY WIRED OUTLET	NORMAL LINE VOLTAGE (U.S. AVG. 117 VAC)	I₁○ ○I₃ I₂●
OPEN GROUND	NORMAL LINE VOLTAGE	I₁● ○I₃ I₂●
OPEN HOT WIRE	ZERO	I₁● ●I₃ I₂●
OPEN NEUTRAL WIRE	ZERO	I₁○ ●I₃ I₂●
HOT-NEUTRAL REVERSED	NORMAL LINE VOLTAGE	I₁● ○I₃ I₂○
HOT-GROUND REVERSED	ZERO	I₁○ ●I₃ I₂○

LEGEND: ○ LAMP ON ● LAMP OFF

PARTS LIST

I1, I2, I3,—Set of three neon indicator lamps with built-in dropping resistors

M1—0-150-v.a.c. voltmeter

Misc.—Phenolic case with 5⅝ x 2⅞ x 2-in. panel; three-wire line cord with U-ground plug; solder.

■ ARE YOUR GROUNDED OUTLETS really grounded? Will the center screw of your ungrounded outlet be a safe connection for the pigtail ground wire of a three-wire adapter plug? Is the outlet's polarity correct? And what's your line voltage? Plug in this easy-to-build checker and you'll have all the answers.

Like commercial testers, it has three lights to indicate polarity. But because it also has an extension plug, you can read it easily even when your outlet is difficult to see or reach. And it checks voltage, too.

Parts are all readily available, and construction is simple. Take care when making the holes in the case. For the meter hole, drill a ring of small holes first, then carefully chip out the material between them. Holes for indicator lamps are first drilled small, then carefully reamed to size to avoid cracking the panel.

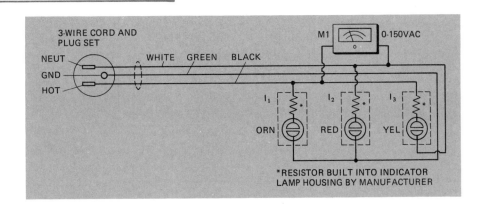

Light control for close jobs

THE LIGHT CONTROL shown is tested for use with a No. 1 photoflood lamp on a workbench.

■ AT TIMES when you're doing close work in the shop, a brighter-than-normal worklight would contribute to greater accuracy. This light-control unit regulates a high-wattage incandescent lamp. Most of the time the control holds the illumination at a comfortable working level. When you need more light, twist the control knob to bring the lamp up to its maximum brightness.

The light control shown is intended for mounting on a wall, ceiling or elsewhere within convenient reach from the workspot. The main components of the control are a push on-off dimmer switch of 600-w rating and a grounded duplex outlet that accepts two- or three-prong plugs.

House these two parts in a pair of surface-mounted steel outlet boxes fastened to a plywood base. You can simplify the arrangement by using one double duplex box and a combination outlet-switch plate. The two boxes shown here are linked by a piece of No. 10 copper wire so they both will be grounded. If made with two boxes, remove adjacent knockouts where the wires will pass through, and smooth the edges of the holes with a rattail file. Fasten the boxes firmly to the mounting base.

A length of No. 16, three-wire flexible cord brings power to the unit from a conventional outlet. If the power supply outlet isn't grounded, provide the unit with a wire connected to one of the screws holding the box-connecting link, and to a water pipe or other suitable ground.

Attach the wall plug so the dimmer switch is in the power side of the circuit (black wire in the diagram). The black wire should be attached to the brass-colored plug tine, which goes into the small slot in the wall outlet.

Be sure the dimmer you use is rated to handle the wattage of your worklight. This control is *not* suitable for fluorescent lights.

COMPLETED LIGHT BOX IS ready for mounting on a wall or other surface. Note box-connecting link near power cord clamp.

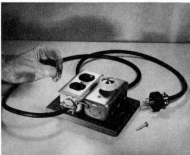

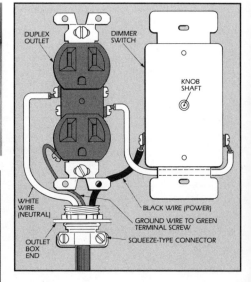

DUPLEX OUTLET

DIMMER SWITCH

KNOB SHAFT

WHITE WIRE (NEUTRAL)

BLACK WIRE (POWER)

GROUND WIRE TO GREEN TERMINAL SCREW

OUTLET BOX END

SQUEEZE-TYPE CONNECTOR

MATERIALS LIST
DIMMER CONTROL

No. Description

1	Dimmer-switch, 600-w rating at 120 v.a.c., push-on action
1	Duplex outlet, grounded, 15-amp., preferably heavy-duty
2	Outlet boxes, surface-mounted, steel (or use one double-duplex, steel, surface-mounted box)*
1	Toggle-switch plate for dimmer-switch box*

1	Duplex outlet plate for outlet box*
1	Squeeze-type cable connector
1	No. 16, three-wire flexible cord, length as needed
1	Grounded three-prong plug
1	No. 10 copper wire (bare), cut to length required by screw spacing, to link boxes
1	½ x 4½ x 5½" wood base or similar

Misc.: Screws as required, No. 12 insulated wire
* If you use a double-duplex, surface-mounted outlet box, you can use a combination toggle-duplex outlet cover.

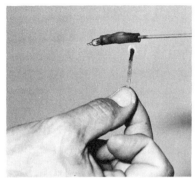

WANT YOUR CB antenna to light up when you transmit? All it takes is one neon bulb and a piece of heat-shrink tubing costing less than a dollar. The bulb, at the tip of your antenna, will blink on and off as you talk.

Tell the world you're on the air

■ YOU MAY NEVER KNOW how this flashing antenna light works. But it sure is fun and it's a cinch to make. It uses only a small neon bulb mounted on top of the antenna. It needs no electrical power because it's activated by radio waves when you transmit. The bulb is the kind you find glowing in household voltage testers. The Radio Shack bulbs, two on a card, cost about 50 cents. Radio Shack also has the "shrink tubing" used to keep the light in place on top of the antenna.

The modification couldn't be simpler. The first step is to try the bulb in place to make sure you have the right kind. Just wrap *one* of the wires from the bulb (not two) around the antenna and stick some masking tape over it. Key the mike with the radio on and the light should glow. If it does, clip the second wire off and get ready to mount it. If it doesn't, continue your search for the right type of neon bulb. Remember, the kind with a filament won't work.

After you've checked out the bulb, position it at the very top of the antenna and tape it in place. Double check by keying the mike and, if the bulb

lights, position the shrink tubing so that it covers the bottom part of the bulb and the end of the antenna. Hold a match near the tubing and carefully shrink the tubing so that it grips the bulb and the end of the antenna.

The final step, of course, is to check your signal-strength meter. Since the length of the antenna has been changed slightly, you may need an adjustment. If so, it is a five-minute operation any CB technician can perform. You should have this done every six months or so anyway in order to maintain maximum performance from your set.

The rest is all fun. Several members of the local van club have added antenna lights, and it's fascinating to watch a convoy of 10 or 12 vans, going down a long, dark highway, twinkling back and forth to each other. The bulb blinks on and off as your voice peaks the power output from your transmitter. Make sure, though, that everything you do about your rig is legal because "Uncle Charley" will now know who is transmitting, for certain, Good Buddy. 10-4?

Put a tester in your screwdriver

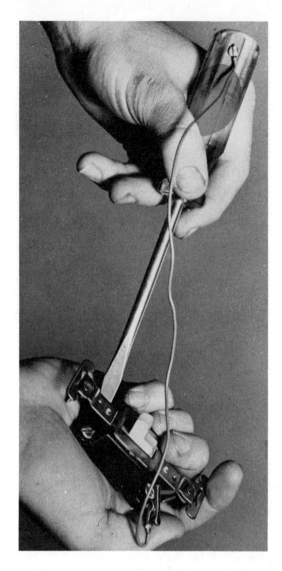

■ LIKE HAVING A COMB on the end of a brush, a continuity tester in the handle of a screwdriver is a natural when it comes to electrical troubleshooting.

A continuity tester consists of a battery and a bulb arranged in series with a pair of test leads. Any device placed in series across these leads, which completes the circuit, will light the bulb. Conversely, if the circuit being tested is "open" or incomplete, the bulb will not light. Suppose, for example, you have a fuse that is questionable. Connect it across the tester. If the bulb lights, the fuse is good.

In addition to fuses you can trace circuit continuity of motors, coils, switches and other devices. You can also check for grounded circuits or apparatus by inserting the tester between the suspected terminals and "ground"; in most cases this is the metal frame. Always be sure, however, that the circuit being tested is disconnected from any external power.

To make such a two-in-one tool, pick a screwdriver that has a clear plastic handle. Since you will be drilling a ⅝-in. hole, buy one that has a 1¼-in.-dia. handle. Also select one that has a minimum of 2½ in. between the end of the embedded shank and the end of the handle.

The handle is counterbored with three different-sized drills, starting with a ⅝-in. bit, then a ⅜-in. one and finally a ¹/₁₆-in. drill. As the detail shows, the ⅝-in. hole is made deep enough to hold two mercury hearing-aid cells and a plastic plug. The ⅜-in. hole is for a spring and a bulb from a two-cell penlight, while the ¹/₁₆-in. hole is for a wire which makes electrical contact with the shank. Where a regular tester has two test leads, this combination screwdriver-tester makes use of the blade for one lead. The deep ¹/₁₆-in. hole is drilled in the soft plastic with a homemade drill made from a piece of wire. Two sides are filed flat for a distance from the end and then sharpened like the end of a conventional metal-cutting drill. This will do the trick but you'll have to back it out often in order to keep the hole cleared of chips.

The spring is made of light wire (about .025-in.) and formed around a ¼-in. dowel so only the nose part of the bulb can enter. One end of the spring gets soldered to the shell of the bulb, while the other end is inserted into the ¹/₁₆-in. hole to make contact with the screwdriver shank. The batteries are inserted with the button of the first battery in contact with the bulb. Here you should have about ⅛ in. of extra space so that the end plug, when pressed in place, will push the batteries and bulb against the spring.

Next a ³/₁₆-in. hole is drilled crosswise through the plug and handle for a plastic rod or

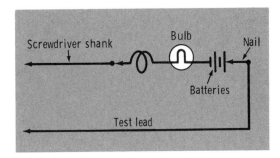

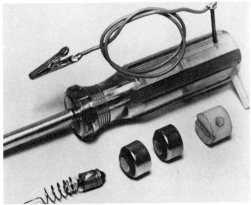

PLASTIC PLUG is held in place by dowel or plastic rod. Slit in plug is a keyway for nail contact.

wooden dowel. The purpose of the plug is to make certain that, should the screwdriver contact a live electrical circuit during use, the voltage potential available through the spring, bulb and batteries will not come in direct contact with the hand. A rubber crutch tip pressed over the end of the handle will provide additional insulation and safety.

At the point where the plug contacts the batteries, drill a ⅛-in. hole for the test-lead tip which is a 7d box nail. Since the hole becomes more of a V-groove across the end of the plug, you'll do best to remove the plug and form the groove with a small round file. A length of stranded wire (18 or 20-ga.) is soldered to the cutoff nail and to an alligator clip. When inserted, the pointed nail contacts the batteries, readying the tester for use.

When it's not in use, keep the test tip out of the handle. This will conserve the batteries. With the test lead removed and the crutch tip in place, contact of the blade with high voltage will not damage either the bulb or batteries because the circuit is no longer complete.

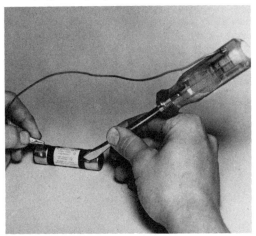

THE SCREWDRIVER SHANK is one probe, the wire with the alligator clip is the other. The glowing light means that the fuse being tested is good.

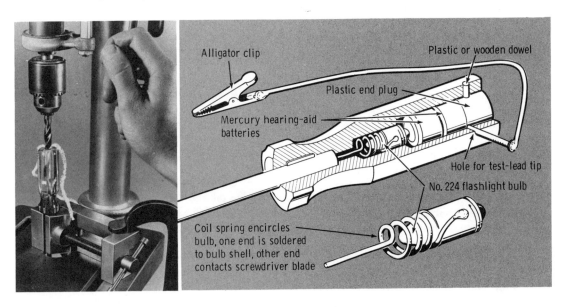

Alligator clip
Plastic or wooden dowel
Plastic end plug
Mercury hearing-aid batteries
Hole for test-lead tip
No. 224 flashlight bulb
Coil spring encircles bulb, one end is soldered to bulb shell, other end contacts screwdriver blade

Emissions controls service

■ IT MAKES GOOD sense to maintain emissions controls periodically from the time a car is new. In addition to increasing air pollution levels, neglected emissions control devices cause poor gasoline mileage, hard starting, stalling, hesitation on acceleration, and dieseling. Dieseling is engine run-on after the ignition is turned off.

Servicing the following emissions control units falls within the skills of a Saturday mechanic:
■ Positive crankcase ventilation (PCV) valve, hoses and filter.
■ Thermostatic control valve in the air cleaner snorkel.
■ Exhaust gas recirculation (EGR) valve.

How to service the PCV system

If the PCV system gets blocked, pressure builds up in the crankcase and may force oil out of the oil filter tube and past the engine oil seals. The result is loss of oil. Naturally, a clogged PCV system also contributes to air pollution.

The heart of the PCV system is the PCV valve, which controls the rate at which vapors in the engine crankcase are allowed to return to the intake manifold. If the PCV valve sticks on the vacuum side of the valve, the flow of air through the valve is restricted. This enriches the air/fuel mixture entering the cylinders, reducing fuel mileage.

If the PCV valve sticks in mid-position, too much air passes through the valve. This makes the fuel mixture too lean and causes rough engine idling. If the valve sticks so it can't move back to close the crankcase port, an engine backfire may cause an explosion in the crankcase.

A combination of shaking the checking for vacuum usually reveals whether a faulty PCV valve exists. When you tune up the engine, do this test:

1. Pull the PCV valve from its position in the valve cover or intake manifold. Shake the valve. If it rattles, it generally indicates a functioning valve. However, this is not a foolproof test.

2. Start the engine and cover the end of the valve with your thumb. If there is no vacuum ("pull" on your thumb), the valve may be plugged or the PCV system hoses may be blocked.

3. Remove and clean out the hoses. This can be done by ramming a cloth wad through them. If hoses are cracked or have hardened, replace them.

4. Test for vacuum after the hoses are reconnected. If there is still no vacuum, replace the PCV valve.

Sludge can be cleaned from a PCV valve by shooting in PCV cleaner. However, there is no way to determine accurately if the spring inside the valve is weak and no longer metering out the proper volume of air. For this reason, car manufacturers recommend replacing the valve every year.

A part of the PCV system often overlooked is the PCV inlet filter, which is generally positioned in the side of the main body of the air cleaner. This filter cleans the air before it enters the crankcase and should be replaced at the same time as the air cleaner filter.

In some cars, the filter pad may be lifted out of a small pocket in the air cleaner. With most installations, the following procedure is necessary.

1. Snap out the retaining clip that holds the PCV filter container to the air cleaner. This clip is at the end of the PCV hose connected to the filter.

2. Remove the container.

3. If possible, take the filter pad from the container. Discard the filter. In some cases, the entire assembly has to be replaced.

4. Wash the container and let it stand until dry.

5. Oil the new filter pad sparingly with your engine oil and then place it into the container.

6. Attach the container to the air cleaner with the retaining clip.

Testing thermostatic control valves

The thermostatic control valve in the air cleaner snorkel controls the temperature of air

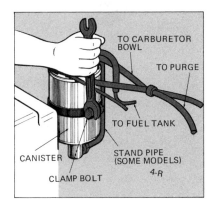

TO CARBURETOR BOWL

TO PURGE

TO FUEL TANK

CANISTER

STAND PIPE (SOME MODELS)

CLAMP BOLT

4-R

entering the carburetor during cold weather. Maintaining temperature within tight limits makes it possible to calibrate the carburetor on the lean side. This reduces hydrocarbon emissions, improves engine warm-up and cuts down on the chance of the carburetor icing during the warm-up period.

This system, which is sometimes referred to as the heated inlet air system, consists of a vacuum diaphragm that sits on top of the air cleaner snorkel, a temperature sensor which is located inside the air cleaner and a control valve installed in the snorkel. These are the steps to follow.

1. Check the functioning of the system with the engine cold and the air temperature below 50° F. Remove the duct connected to the snorkel, If there is one, and put your hand inside the snorkel. See that the control valve moves freely.

2. Start the engine. As the engine warms up, the valve should move in the direction opposite to that when the engine was cold.

3. If the control valve doesn't operate in this way, test the vacuum diaphragm with a vacuum pump. If the vacuum diaphragm functions properly when tested, replace the sensor.

4. Test control-valve action once a year.

How to service the EGR valve

American Motors Corp.:

1. Remove the EGR valve from the engine.

2. Scrape deposits from the valve base using a wire brush.

3. By hand, compress the valve diaphragm to determine if the poppet valve is functioning. This is established by the valve moving freely. If the poppet valve sticks, discard the EGR valve.

AMC recommends this service every 30,000 miles.

Chrysler Corp.:

1. Remove the EGR valve from the engine.

2. Inspect the poppet valve and seat for carbon. If any deposits are discovered, continue servicing as detailed below. If not, reinstall the valve.

3. Apply manifold heat-control valve solvent to the poppet valve and seal, but be careful not to spill solvent on the valve diaphragm. Allow solvent to loosen deposits. If solvent is spilled on the diaphragm, replace the EGR valve. Solvent causes irreparable damage.

4. With a vacuum pump, apply vacuum to the valve vacuum nipple to open the valve. Then, use a knife to scrape off carefully all deposits from the seat and poppet valve.

Chrysler recommends this service every 15,000 miles.

Ford Motor Co.:

1. Remove EGR valve from the engine.

2. Outfit an electric drill with a short piece of speedometer cable. Insert the end of the cable into the valve cavity located between the poppet and the seat.

3. Turn on the drill. Employing a circular motion, loosen deposits.

Food recomments this procedure when one of the following engine problems occurs; rough idling, stalling, rough acceleration under light throttle application, excessive fuel consumption, stalling under deceleration and detonation.

General Motors:

1. Remove the EGR valve.

2. Hold the valve diaphragm down and plug the vacuum tube.

3. Release the diaphragm. The poppet valve should not close until 20 seconds or more have elapsed. If it does, replace the EGR valve.

4. Check for deposits on the poppet valve and seat. If they are present, tap the end of the poppet valve with a plastic hammer and shake deposits from the unit.

5. Look for deposits in outlet holes. Clean them out carefully with a knife or screwdriver.

6. Scrape mounting surfaces for the EGR valve and the engine with a wire brush.

GM recommends this procedure when one of the following engine problems occurs: rough idling, stalling, rough acceleration under light throttle application, excessive fuel consumption, stalling under deceleration and detonation.

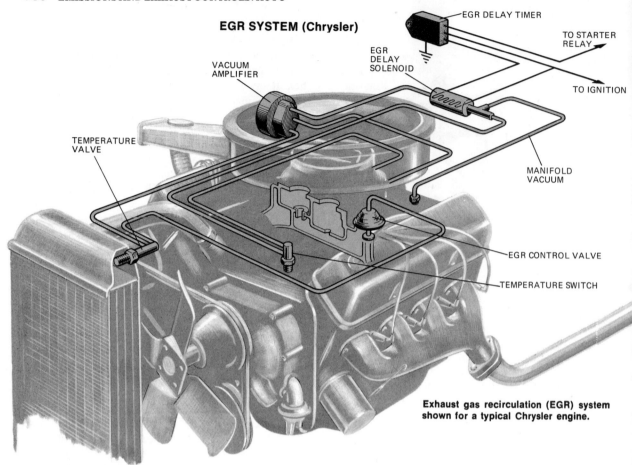

EGR SYSTEM (Chrysler)

EGR DELAY TIMER

TO STARTER RELAY

EGR DELAY SOLENOID

TO IGNITION

VACUUM AMPLIFIER

MANIFOLD VACUUM

TEMPERATURE VALVE

EGR CONTROL VALVE

TEMPERATURE SWITCH

Exhaust gas recirculation (EGR) system shown for a typical Chrysler engine.

Catalytic converter and EGR system service

■ A CATALYTIC converter, which is the muffler-shaped container hung under a car with the exhaust system to cut down on hydrocarbon and carbon monoxide emissions, has a life expectancy of 50,000 miles.

The EGR—shorthand for exhaust gas recirculation—is a means of lowering combustion temperature so oxides of nitrogen, pollutants that develop in a high-temperature environment, are kept in check. This is done by recirculating metered amounts of exhaust back into the combustion chamber, which slows the combustion process and lowers the combustion temperature.

The catalytic converter and EGR system are easy enough to keep in shape. And if you live in a state with mandatory emissions inspection, you don't have a choice.

Types of catalytic converters

There are two types of catalytic converters on U.S.-built cars. One is filled with thousands of alumina pellets. Alumina is an aluminum oxide. Pellets are coated with a combination of platinum-palladium, or platinum-palladium-rhodium catalyzing agent. The other, called a monolithic converter, contains a one-piece extruded honeycomb material that is coated with a platinum or platinum-palladium catalyzing agent.

Monolithic and pellet converters function the same way. The catalyst oxidizes exhaust from the

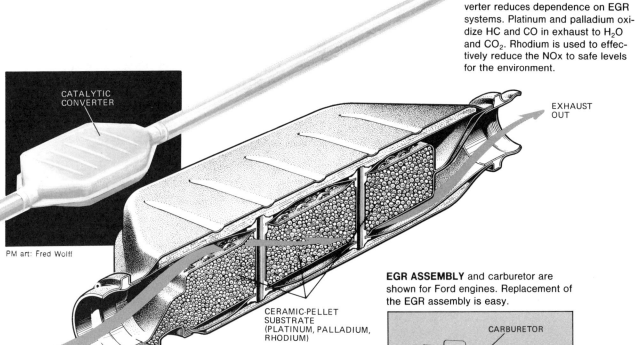

THREE-WAY design catalytic converter reduces dependence on EGR systems. Platinum and palladium oxidize HC and CO in exhaust to H_2O and CO_2. Rhodium is used to effectively reduce the NOx to safe levels for the environment.

CATALYTIC CONVERTER

EXHAUST OUT

PM art: Fred Wolff

CERAMIC-PELLET SUBSTRATE (PLATINUM, PALLADIUM, RHODIUM)

EXHAUST IN

EGR ASSEMBLY and carburetor are shown for Ford engines. Replacement of the EGR assembly is easy.

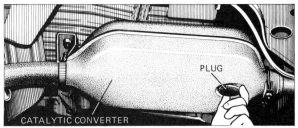

PLUG

CATALYTIC CONVERTER

PELLET-TYPE catalytic converter has a plug on the bottom side. When the converter needs to be rejuvenated, only the pellets need to be replaced. Vacuum pump is used to suck out the spent pellets and then a vibrator tool jiggles the fresh pellets into the converter.

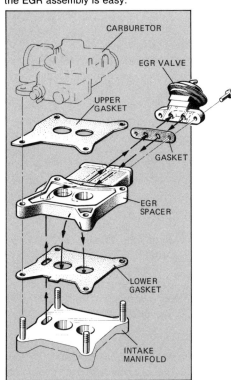

CARBURETOR

EGR VALVE

UPPER GASKET

GASKET

EGR SPACER

LOWER GASKET

INTAKE MANIFOLD

engine into carbon monoxide (CO) and hydrocarbons (HC) into harmless water (H_2O) and carbon dioxide (CO_2).

In the process, the temperature inside the converter rises to a level somewhat higher than that of the exhaust gases. However, insulation inside the converter keeps the outside skin at about the same temperature as the muffler.

The main difference between pellet and monolithic converters, other than construction, is that the pellet converter can be serviced. Pellets can be replaced when they become ineffective. When

EGR VALVE diaphragm pulsations can be felt and are check of good operation.

EGR VALVE

the catalyst-coated honeycomb in a monolithic converter gives out the entire converter is replaced.

Replacement procedures

Perhaps surprisingly so, replacing a monolithic converter is more of a do-it-yourself job than replacing pellets, because no special equipment is needed. The unit is replaced the same way a muffler is replaced. Ironically, however, replacing a monolithic converter yourself (or pellet converter, if necessary) is more expensive than having someone replace pellets.

If you have to replace an entire pellet converter the cost may be high, but this is necessary only when the outside body is distorted.

Distortion (bugle) occurs because excessive heat builds up in the converter—not the converter's fault.

Excessive heat is caused by a carburetor, ignition or air pump problem that permits unburned fuel to enter the converter where it ignites. If a damaged converter is replaced without correcting the problem, the new converter is going to fail prematurely.

If a pellet converter's bottom cover is ripped or dented, you shouldn't have to replace the whole converter, only the bottom cover.

To replace pellets, a threaded or pressed-in plug is removed from the base of the converter. The vacuum pump is attached to suck pellets out and the vibrator, possessing a can of fresh pellets, is attached to pump the new pellets in.

Who's got what

Although there are only two main types of catalytic converters, there are some interesting variations.

Some cars use pellet converters as the main instrument, but they also possess monolithic warm-up converters. Others have monolithic warm-up converters in combination with the main monolithic converters.

A warm-up converter's small size and closeness to the engine cause it to react more rapidly than a main converter to incoming gases. It converts exhaust gases into nonpolluting agents when the engine starts.

Generally, a six-cylinder engine has one warm-up converter between the exhaust manifold and main converter. An eight-cylinder engine has two warm-up converters, one serving each bank of cylinders.

Replacing a used-up warm-up converter is as simple as replacing the main converter. Remove the front exhaust pipe at the exhaust manifold and at the pellet converter joint. The warm-up converter is integral with the front exhaust pipe.

A "phase two" catalyst emission control system controls oxides of nitrogen, as well as hydrocarbons and carbon monoxide (hence it is most-often referred to as a *three-way* catalytic converter).

It reduces dependence on EGR systems and ignition-spark retarding to meet oxides-of-nitrogen standards.

One of the catalyst coatings in a three-way system is rhodium, which controls oxides of nitrogen by separating this polluting agent into harmless nitrogen and oxygen. Unfortunately, rhodium is scarcer and more expensive than platinum and palladium.

The heart of the phase-two system is an electronic fuel control unit, which receives voltage signals from an oxygen sensor in the exhaust system. The sensor tells the control unit if the fuel mixture is too rich or lean. The unit makes the necessary correction at the carburetor. Accurate air/fuel ratio is critical to operation of the system.

The oxygen sensor should be replaced every 15,000 miles. Otherwise, servicing procedures for the phase-two converter are the same as for other pellet converters.

Use only unleaded fuel

By now everyone should know they shouldn't use leaded gasoline in a car that has a catalytic converter. Using a few gallons of leaded gasoline is acceptable to get a car to a gas station that has unleaded fuel.

Constant use of leaded gas will leave combustion deposits, mainly lead, in the converter, producing the same results as a blocked exhaust system—lack of power and limited top speed even at wide open throttle. According to Ford, rust that gets inside a converter from a rusting exhaust manifold will do the same thing.

EGR: the way it works

EGR systems from car to car work pretty much the same. Technically, the system is called PEGR (proportional exhaust gas recirculation), because the design provides exhaust gas recirculation at a rate proportional to engine load.

No exhaust gas recirculation is provided at idle, because none is needed since combustion temperatures are low enough to restrict oxides of nitrogen formation. As the car reaches cruising speed, more EGR is provided as needed.

The job of metering exhaust gases to the air-fuel charge falls to the EGR control valve. The EGR valve, in turn, is controlled by vacuum.

In a typical engine, the vacuum signal is proportional to engine air flow (or load) and is provided by a port in the carburetor venturi. The vacuum signal is applied to a vacuum amplifier, which modulates vacuum in such a manner that output from the amplifier is normally 10 times the magnitude of the input vacuum signal. The amplified signal actuates the EGR valve.

There are other key parts to an EGR system besides the EGR valve—the coolant temperature switch and valve. These eliminate EGR when the engine is cold to provide stable engine operation during warm-up.

Testing the EGR

If a part of the EGR system malfunctions, engine hesitation and/or poor idling result. The main components of a typical system—EGR valve, coolant temperature switch, connecting hose—may be tested as follows:

Caution: The engine has to be at normal operating temperature and the EGR valve may be hot. Be careful not to burn your fingers. You may wish to wear gloves.

1. With the engine idling, hold your fingers against the bottom (diaphragm) of the valve. You may feel a slight vibration—normal in six- and eight-cylinder engines.

2. Accelerate the engine. The diaphragm should open (move upward).

3. Return the engine to idle. The diaphragm should close (move downward).

Note: If the installation prohibits your being able to place your fingers on the diaphragm, watch the EGR valve stem instead. It should move as the engine is accelerated rapidly and is allowed to return to idle.

4. If the diaphragm (valve stem) doesn't move, pull the vacuum hose off the valve. Hold your finger over the end. Accelerate the engine to a speed equivalent to 2000 rpm. You should feel a strong pull. If not, remove the hose and check it for a restriction or cracks.

5. If vacuum is present, remove the EGR valve for cleaning. Or replace the valve.

Note: EGR valves are different from engine to

engine of the same make. Be sure to get the right one.

6. If you are experiencing a driving problem when the engine is cold, and the EGR valve and hose test satisfactorily, test the coolant-temperature switch. With the engine cold, see if vacuum is present at the EGR valve by feeling for suction (Step 4). If it is present (it shouldn't be), replace the switch usually found at thermostat housing or coolant passage.

Specific service problems

■ One reason for poor idling and hesitation for Ford engines can be a burned-out EGR spacer between the carburetor and intake manifold. This would allow a constant flow of exhaust gases into the intake manifold. Replace the spacer, and the upper and lower gaskets.

■ Some AMC four-cylinder engines use a stainless steel restrictor plate between the EGR valve and intake manifold. The plate and the two gaskets that sandwich it are calibrated for a particular engine-exhaust system combination and should not be altered or replaced with any other type of restrictor plate. There is an identification number or letter on every plate. Be sure the new part has the same number or letter as the old part.

A troubling report

One Environmental Protection Agency report emphasizes that emission controls are only as effective as we allow them to be. Reasons for high emissions failure rates given were:

■ Misadjustment of basic engine settings, particularly idle speed, ignition timing and choke.

■ "Willful or inadvertent" disablement of a component or system. Examples include plugged, disconnected or rerouted vacuum lines; "carefully damaged" EGR valves; broken or missing idle mixture limiter caps.

■ Defective components, including leaking vacuum diaphragms, faulty coolant temperature-sensing vacuum switches and timers, broken EGR back-pressure transducers.

■ Inadequate maintenance (dirty air cleaners, worn-out plugs).

■ Using nonspecified parts. Replacement components should match the particular engine and emission control system combination. As an example, replace resistor-type sparkplugs with the same type, instead of using nonresistor plugs.

Exhaust system replacement

■ IF YOU WANT to save money you should replace rotted exhaust system parts or, if necessary, the entire system *yourself.* You can't deny that replacing an exhaust system can be a dirty, sweaty job, but it's worth a little perspiration to save $35 or $40. The toughest part is usually loosening nuts and bolts that have frozen stiff over the miles.

A rack simplifies job

You can tackle exhaust-system replacement lying flat on your back, if you must, but the job is made much easier by getting the car in the air. If you're friendly with a guy at a local gas station or garage, maybe he'll let you use his lift during off-hours. If not, you can place the car's four corners on jack stands. Just make sure the stands are strong enough to take the weight and are properly set.

The exhaust system should be cold when you work to avoid burns.

Every exhaust system has three common parts: exhaust (front) pipe, muffler and tailpipe. Parts are suspended from hangers which are bolted to the undercarriage, and joints where parts meet are usually secured with clamps.

Most cars have one exhaust system, but some with V8 engines have two. A dual exhaust system is nothing more than two identical (or almost identical), but separate single-exhaust systems, one serving the engine's right bank of cylinders and the other serving the left bank.

The front pipe of cars having V8 engines and single exhaust systems is a so-called crossover pipe—a single pipe having two branches.

One branch attaches to the exhaust manifold on the right side of the engine, and the other attaches to the exhaust manifold on the left side. Exhaust feeds from both branches into the common pipe and out through one system.

Many cars also have resonators, which are merely second mufflers, smaller than the main muffler, that help further reduce engine noise.

Don't damage valuable parts

A catalytic converter is part of the exhaust system, but most times other exhaust parts fail much faster than a converter which is designed to last 50,000 miles.

This means that in replacing an exhaust system having a catalytic converter you have to exercise care not to damage the converter when taking it from the car and when reinstalling it.

Also watch how you handle long exhaust pipes and tailpipes that are still in usable condition when disconnecting them to replace a shot muffler. When releasing one end of the pipe and shifting to the other end to make a disconnection, support the pipe by wrapping a length of soft wire around it and tying it to a rail or cross-member. This keeps the pipe straight and stops it from bending.

After new and/or reusable parts are put back together, spread a liberal quantity of exhaust-system joint sealer around the joints before you tighten the clamps. The sealer, not the clamp, prevents the joint from leaking.

Up front where you may have to remove the exhaust pipe from the exhaust manifold, there

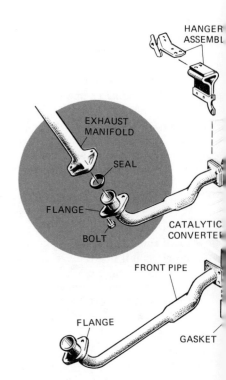

may be a gasket. If there is, throw it away and replace with a new gasket.

If you have a torque wrench and are able to get your hands on manufacturer's tightening torques for fasteners (specs are given in service manuals), use it. However, a torque wrench isn't really necessary. But caution is.

Use care in tightening

Tighten fasteners securely—that is, enough to keep parts from moving and banging against the undercarriage. But don't tighten them to a point where you'll crush pipes.

To give you guidance in replacing an exhaust system, here are directions to follow when doing the job on Valiants and Darts with six-cylinder engines and without catalytic converters; and on Granadas, Monarchs, Comets and Mavericks with eight-cylinder engines, single exhaust systems and no catalytic converters.

Procedures basically similar

No matter what kind of car you own, you will find many similarities and few minor differences between the procedure you have to use and the procedures outlined here.

To replace the exhaust systems of Valiants and Darts with six-cylinder engines and without catalytic converters:

1. Disconnect the two nuts holding the exhaust pipe flange to the exhaust manifold. Discard the gasket.

2. Remove the two U-bolt nuts of the U-bolt holding the front of the exhaust pipe at its neck.

3. Inspect the exhaust pipe U-bolt and U-bolt hanger assembly, and replace it if damaged or deteriorated.

4. Turn your attention to the muffler, and note that the muffler and exhaust pipe in this car is an integral, one-piece assembly. When you have to replace one, you have to replace both.

5. At the rear of the muffler, remove the U-bolt holding the muffler and tailpipe together, and slide the muffler forward, disengaging it from the tailpipe. Lower the muffler and exhaust-pipe

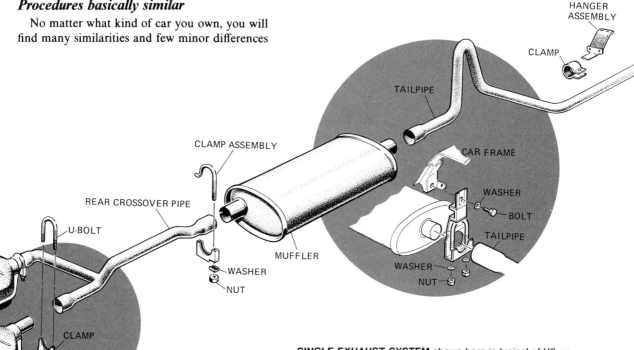

SINGLE EXHAUST SYSTEM shown here is typical of V8 engine with two catalytic converters, one serving the right bank of cylinders and the other the left. Both feed exhaust into a single muffler and tailpipe. Detail views show hanger assemblies and clamps typically used to secure parts and to hang system from car frame. Make sure you have all the parts you need before starting the job and remember that you won't be able to get close enough to these red-hot parts to start work if you've just used the car!

assembly to the ground.

6. Inspect the muffler-tailpipe U-bolt and U-bolt hanger; replace it if damaged or deteriorated.

7. Remove the bolt holding the tailpipe support to the car's frame and lower the tailpipe to the ground.

Some models have a resonator as an integral part of the tailpipe. If either has been damaged, both have to be replaced.

8. Inspect the tailpipe support, and replace it with a new one if the support is damaged or deteriorated.

9. Begin installation by attaching the exhaust pipe to its U-bolt. Engage the U-bolt nuts loosely.

Caution: If the exhaust pipe and muffler are an integrated unit, be sure to support the muffler in some way as you work on the exhaust pipe, so the muffler doesn't fall and get damaged.

10. Install a new gasket at the exhaust pipe flange and exhaust manifold connection. Engage the two connecting nuts loosely.

11. Notice the small pipe extension at the rear of the muffler. Engage it in its U-bolt hanger assembly and connect it to the tailpipe as securely as possible.

12. Secure the tailpipe to its support, engaging the bolt loosely.

13. Install the U-bolt at the muffler-tailpipe joint and engage the two U-bolt nuts loosely.

14. Coat all joints with exhaust-system sealer, and make certain the entire exhaust system is properly aligned so there is no strain on any part before tightening fasteners. If you have a torque wrench, here are the specifications to follow:

■ Exhaust pipe-to-exhaust manifold nuts: 35 ft.-lb.

■ Exhaust pipe U-bolt nuts: 95 in.-lb.

■ Muffler-to-tailpipe U-bolt nuts: 150 in.-lb.

■ Tailpipe support bolt: 200 in.-lb.

Tackling 8-cylinder systems

To replace the exhaust systems of Granadas, Monarchs, Comets and Mavericks with eight-cylinder engines, single exhausts and no catalytic converters:

1. At about the middle of the crossover pipe, remove fasteners from the hanger that holds the pipe. Support the pipe to keep it from falling and being damaged as you continue your work elsewhere if the pipe can be salvaged.

2. Remove the nuts attaching the crossover pipe to the resonator inlet pipe, and remove the nuts attaching the crossover pipe flanges to the

exhaust manifolds. This releases the crossover pipe, which can now be removed.

3. Notice that if this is the car's original exhaust system the resonator inlet pipe, resonator, resonator-to-muffler pipe, muffler and tailpipe are all welded together in an integrated unit. It is removed by removing the two bolts holding the resonator to its hanger assembly at the rear of the resonator.

4. At the rear of the muffler, loosen and remove the two bolts holding the muffler-tailpipe to its hanger assembly. The assembly is now free and can be removed.

5. Inspect hangers and replace any which look shot.

Important: Replacement exhaust system parts for these cars are normally provided in separate, rather than integrated pieces, which are secured together with clamps. The parts normally furnished are exhaust pipe, resonator and resonator inlet pipe, muffler-tailpipe assembly, and crossover pipe.

6. Begin reassembly by attaching the crossover pipe loosely to its hanger and connecting the crossover pipe flanges loosely to the exhaust manifolds.

7. Connect the resonator inlet pipe-resonator assembly to the rear of the crossover pipe. Coat the joint with exhaust-system sealer and attach the clamp loosely.

8. Attach resonator to hanger and secure the fasteners loosely.

9. Connect the front of the resonator-to-muffler pipe to the rear of the muffler, coat the joint with exhaust system sealer and attach the clamp loosely.

10. Attach the muffler-tailpipe assembly to its hanger and secure bolts loosely.

11. Join the rear of the resonator-to-muffler pipe to the front of the muffler, coat the joint with sealer and secure with a clamp.

12. Make sure the exhaust system is aligned straight and true so there's no strain on any point, and tighten fasteners securely. If you have a torque wrench, here are the torque values to abide by:

■ Crossover pipe-to-exhaust manifold nuts: 25-35 ft.-lb.

■ Crossover pipe support bracket nuts: 8-14 ft.-lb.

■ Exhaust pipe-to-resonator inlet pipe flange: 20-30 ft.-lb.

■ Resonator-to-resonator hanger bolts: 10-20 ft.-lb.

■ Muffler-to-muffler hanger bolts: 8-14 ft.-lb.

Home energy costs cut

■ THE ENERGY CRISIS is hardly news, and few doubt its seriousness. It's grimly reflected every month when bills arrive. The news is full of grandiose plans for the year 2000, and enterpreneurs keep devising systems for homeowners that would cost nearly as much as the housing itself—with little hope of amortizing such expense in a normal lifetime. So far, there's been little useful information about how the average homeowner can beat soaring utility and heating bills.

Are there any ways to beat the system? You bet there are! The first step is to take a look at where energy goes in a normal American home. The figures are well established. Some 70 percent goes to heat and/or to cool the house; 20 percent heats water; 10 percent runs lighting and appliances.

With that for starters, here are 101 *practical* things you can do *right now* to slash the local utility company's bite, and soaring home fuel bills, by up to half or more. Many cost nothing at all; others involve minor expense for simple projects, most of which you can build or install yourself; a few require sensible investment that will pay for itself over a few years of use. All have been tested and proven for the U.S. Department of Energy (DOE), by scientific laboratories in universities or in industrial labs.

Things to do without building or installing anything

■ Keep daytime thermostats at 65 °F. in winter and (if you have central airconditioning) at 78° in summer. Both limits fall within a good health range. "People who insist they're pneumonia bait at anything below 75° in winter," say scientists, "are the same ones who cry 'heat prostration' in summer if the airconditioner is set above 65°." You'll save 3 percent of fuel costs for every degree the *average* house temperature is cut.
■ Drop your 'stat to 55° when you retire in winter. The fuel bill will drop one percent for every degree dialed down at night.
■ Remove radiator covers (or use perforated tops) if your system is steam or hot water. Radiators create special convection currents in front of windows and outside walls. Covers decrease their efficiency.

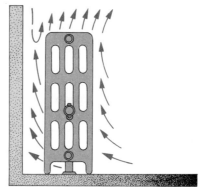

REMOVE radiator covers to let heat convection function more efficiently.

■ For maximum efficiency, use flat paint on radiators and dust them regularly. Dust and metallic paints are insulators.
■ Protect your thermostat from drafts. If it's near a frequently used fireplace, move it to a more distant inside wall. Fireplace heat will keep it from triggering the furnace and distant rooms will get too cold, wasting fuel to get them back to proper temperature.
■ "Zone control" your home manually by closing off unused rooms and turning off their radiators (or shutting registers). Use self-sticking foam weatherstrip to seal such doors to prevent air exchange either way. Similar zone control can be realized with central airconditioning in summer.
■ In hot-air systems, replace the filter monthly during the heating season. A dirty filter reduces efficiency.
■ Check ductwork for leaks and tape any loose seams or joints.
■ Have your furnace serviced annually by a professional and make sure he checks—and adjusts if necessary—the burning rate.
■ Hang drapes on all windows where practical; close them at nigh in winter months.
■ Double-hung windows with storm sash on an unshaded south wall can serve as solar collectors in the winter. Open the inside window a few inches (no more than three or four) from top and bottom. The greenhouse effect of the storm sash will warm air between the panes and set up a chimney that heats low-lying room air coming in at the bottom and sends it back through the open top 20° or more warmer.
■ Turn off ventilating fans in kitchen or bath when they've done their job. They can empty a house of warm air in one hour.

Water heaters
■ Repair leaky faucets. One drop per second

wastes 60 gallons of expensively heated water per week.

■ Set hot water tank at 120°—"medium" on some heaters—not the usual 140°. It will be plenty warm, and you'll cut 20 percent from the cost of hot water—which accounts for 20 percent of your total heating bill.

■ Use cold water to flush away food in the sink garbage disposer. It works better than hot water; grease particles flush out and there's no buildup in pipes.

Fireplaces

■ With a fireplace going, keep doors to other rooms closed—or keep the furnace turned off until you need it.

■ If the thermostat faces a frequently used fireplace, or is close by, move it to the far end of an inside wall or to another room with no alternate heat source.

■ Keep the fireplace damper closed when no fire is burning. An open flue from a 48-inch-square fireplace opening will remove 8 percent of furnace-warmed air from the house continually.

■ Fasten a metal handle to the bottom of a five-gallon enamel canning pot and (wearing an insulated glove) use it as a snuffer to extinguish a live-embers (not blazing) fire when you leave the fireplace. *Be sure all live coals* are extinguished before you close the damper.

Airconditioning

■ Set your thermostat at 78°, which can be comfortable if you dress lightly. If your usual setting was 72° you'll save between 12 and 14 percent (depending on your area) of the annual bill for cooling.

■ Don't set the thermostat colder "to get it started" on the theory that it will cool the room sooner. It won't.

■ Change your airconditioner's filter monthly during the cooling seson. Dirt slows movement of cool air into the house.

■ Keep the airconditioner's fan on "high" except in humid weather. The compressor works just as hard whether the fan is high or low. On high, more cooled air is brought into the house and the compressor will shut itself off sooner.

■ Spread cooled air around your room with a small portable fan. It keeps the cooled air from "layering" and settling to the floor.

■ Turn off a room airconditioner when you leave the room. You'll use less current bringing the temperature down again when you return than if you left it running.

■ Don't locate lamps, TV or radio near enough to affect the airconditioner's thermostatic control, which is highly sensitive.

■ Keep direct sunlight from entering an airconditioned room. This is readily achieved by drawing drapes and closing blinds or shades. Such simple measures can reduce the sun's heat input into a room by up to 80 percent.

■ Keep windows and outside doors shut when temperature outside is higher than inside.

■ If you use storm windows in winter, leave them up in summer. The double glass has an insulating effect that can cut heat infiltration by more than half.

■ Keep lights off whenever possible while the airconditioner is running, and use lamps with as low wattage as possible when you need light. Incandescent lamps add considerable heat for the airconditioner to get rid of.

Lighting

■ Use one large bulb in preference to three smaller ones where bright light is needed. A 100-watt lamp will provide better reading light than three 40-watt bulbs.

■ "Long life" incandescents use more energy than standard bulbs. Enough said.

■ Turn off all but one or two low-watt lamps when watching TV. You only need enough light to balance TV brightness and avoid eyestrain.

■ Specify 4-watt clear night-light bulbs. They use half the energy of the 7-watters and provide almost the same light.

■ Keep all bulbs and shades clean. Dirt absorbs light.

■ Use outdoor spots, floods and driveway illumination only when necessary.

■ Use fluorescent bulbs whenever possible. A 40-watt fluorescent will use 140 watts less than a 60-watt incandescent in a seven-hour period—and provide more than five times the amount of light.

Kitchen

■ Never boil water in an open pan. It boils sooner and over less heat in a covered vessel. Once boiling, keep it rolling with as low a flame as possible. Unpressurized boiling water gets little hotter, no matter how high the flame.

■ Kept clean, range-top burners and reflectors produce more heat with less energy.

■ Don't put small pans on large heating elements or (on gas stoves) let flame exceed diameter of the pan. Heat missing the pot bottom is lost to the air.

■ Turn off heating elements of electric stoves shortly before cooking time is up. They'll stay hot long enough to finish the job without using more electricity.

■ Don't open the oven door to "peek and poke." It wastes heat. Use a timer for baking and roasting.

■ Small electric fry pans and grills use less energy than a range or oven for small meals. A toaster uses less power than the oven or grill for family toast.

■ Keep the refrigerator food compartment at 40°; freezer compartment at 5°. A thermometer will give you the proper setting for the unit's dial control.

■ Manual-defrost refrigerators and freezers should be defrosted regularly. More than a ¼-inch buildup of frost puts an extra load on the compressor motor.

■ Check seals on refrigerator and freezer doors. If you can slip a piece of paper under them anywhere, have them replaced.

■ Don't wash dishes under hot running water or you'll be throwing away gallons of costly heated water. Close the drain, fill the sink with warm water and detergent, and rinse with a hot spray in the dish drainer.

■ Never run your dishwasher until it has a full load.

■ If your washer has no "air-dry" switch, turn the control to "off" position after the last rinse, crack the door and let the dishes air-dry by themselves. You'll save a third of the energy cost of automatic dishwashing.

■ The "rinse-hold" control on dishwashers use three to seven gallons of hot water each time used. Avoid using it.

Laundry

■ Don't wash partial loads. Wait until you can fill the machine—unless it has a "small load" attachment.

■ Always presoak badly soiled clothes, or use the soak cycle to avoid having to run a wash twice.

■ Clothes can be cleaned successfully in warm water rather than "hot" water, and can be rinsed well in cold water. You'll save half the demand on the water heater with these easy steps.

■ Don't let lint build up the dryer's collector screen. It blocks airflow and takes more time and heat to do the job.

■ Don't forget the old-fashioned clothesline. Outdoors in fine weather clothes get a fresh sunshine smell. On bad winter days, hang them in a basement area warmed by the furnace. That dryer—gas or electric—uses a phenomenal amount of energy.

■ Dry heavy and lightweight laundry separately if there's enough wash for two loads. Light clothes dry faster, use less energy. They may even dry with residual heat left from the first batch.

Bathroom

■ Try five-minute showers instead of 30-minute tub baths. You'll use 25 percent less hot water. In a year it can amount to nearly $50 for a family of four in water heating cost.

■ Don't scrub nails or wash hands under a running stream. Fill sink for washing and rinsing. You'll use half as much heated water.

Insulation

■ The DOE estimates that some 40 million single-family homes in this country are inadequately insulated. By bringing them up to par, the heating and cooling load for each home could be reduced by 20 to 30 percent. That means that if your home heating bill runs to $800, a $600 investment in insulation could pay for itself in three to five years.

Check where and how much insulation your house may need. Local building materials dealers can provide the insulation "R-values" recommended for your area. The "R" stands for resistance to heat loss (or heat gain, in summer). The amount of resistance provided by the thickness of any particular insulating material is expressed by a number; the higher the number, the higher the insulating, or resistance, value. All building materials have *some* insulating value including walls with no insulation at all. But such R-values are quite low (see the chart for the thickness required in different types of insulation to produce a given R-value).

■ Check attic insulation, where most heat loss occurs in a house. DOE recommends R-30 (9 to

ATTIC CALLS for R-30 insulation. Add more to bring it up.

10 inches of batts or blanket type). It's best installed between ceiling joists, and can be layered if you already have some but not enough. It can cut 5 percent from your heating bill if you add 3 or 4 inches to bring it up; up to 30 percent if you're starting from scratch.

■ As for walls, DOE tests show that electrical gear, braces and firestops block blown-in insulation, leaving huge voids, and that blow-in and foaming types are too expensive for dollar payback in a reasonable time. It will cut some heat loss if you retrofit exterior walls. If you do, R-11 to 13 is recommended. Be sure to have the installer put vents in the wall for moisture control. Insulated walls can save you 16 to 20 percent in heating costs.

■ Insulate basement or crawl-space walls—it's worth a 5 to 25-percent saving, depending on weather-tightness of your home's underpinnings, and will also protect water pipes against frost. This can be done outside by digging trenches and laying in one-inch foam panels, as shown, against the exterior side of the basement or crawl-space wall, or on the wall's interior side with blanket-type insulation. While the foams have a much higher R-value per inch of thickness, they are not often used inside due to the combustible properties of most. Urethanes are very flammable. Ureas are less so, but their insulating value drops somewhat with time.

■ Insulating a water heater can save another 5 to 12 percent in heating cost. Johns-Manville puts out special blanket kits for electric or gas-type heaters. Keep all gas-heater vents exposed.

HOT-AIR DUCT TAPE, a product of companies like 3M, is used to seal every seam and gap in metal work. Installers frequently miss a lot of places.

Caulking and weatherstripping

Up to 70 percent of heat loss in poorly built homes can be due to infiltration of outside air through window and door frames. Caulking and weatherstripping materials for an average three-bedroom home may cost as little as $25. Savings in costs for heat can run to 10 percent or more per year.

■ Insulate ducts and pipes. Long runs of sheet-metal ducting and hot-water pipe can lose more heat on the way to destinations than they deliver there. Special two-inch blanket-type insulation is made for ductwork; asbestos sleeve sections are available for all water-pipe diameters. Together,

IN COLD basements or crawl spaces, blanket-type insulation should be used to wrap metal ducting as shown above. In heated basements, or in areas where water pipes may freeze, don't wrap the ducts.

BLANKET-TYPE insulation is used as shown in basements and crawl spaces, with a strip against the header joist between the floor and sill, and strips cleated to the sill and draped down the wall.

they can cut from 5 to 10 percent of your yearly heating bill.

■ Run a lighted candle around the inside of all window and door frames. If the flame dances, you need calking. If it leans away from window sash edges, and if you can slide heavy paper under the door, you need weatherstripping.

All joints where two different materials, or sections of the house, meet should be caulked.

■ Caulk along window and door tops between the drip caps and siding . . .

■ Caulk along the joints between window and door frames and siding . . .

■ Caulk along the underside of windowsills where they butt the siding . . .

■ Caulk all inside and outside corner joints that are formed by the siding . . .

■ Caulk along the underside of the siding, where it laps the foundation wall . . .

■ Caulk around hose bibs and other outside wall penetrations by pipes, elecrical service conduits, dryer vents, ventilator housings and so forth.

■ Caulk where pipes and wires penetrate ceilings from an unheated attic . . .

■ Caulk along joints where chimney and other masonry meet siding . . .

■ Caulk along joints where the porch decks and roofs meet the siding . . .

■ Caulk along joints where the gable ends meet the roof eaves.

■ Check all window panes and apply glazing compound where old putty has hardened and cracked or broken off.

■ Weatherstrip all outside windows and doors. Cheapest and easiest to install is the self-sticking foam strip, but it should be replaced every couple of years. It won't stand up, either, along the sides of double-hung windows where friction of raising and lowering the sash induces heavy wear.

Rolled vinyl stops are readily tacked in place by do-it-yourselfers for a longer-lasting seal. Spring metal makes a snug, durable seal, but calls for precise placement and handling. Metal J-stripping is the best of all, but requires removal of doors and windows and highly critical alignment; it's really a job for a professional.

■ Install sealed thresholds under outside doors. "Sweep" types are easily tacked in place on the outside surface of the door bottom by anyone who can swing a hammer, but may wear the carpet where they rub across it when you open and close the door. Vinyl bulb types are better, but tougher to install; interlocking metal units are excellent, but need critical alignment. The latter two types require removal of the door and refitting its bottom.

■ Weatherstrip the attic door if you have one, or icy air from up there will pour down in a continuous stream to chill expensively warmed rooms below.

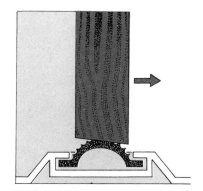

VINYL BULB threshold for exterior doors is efficient and replaceable.

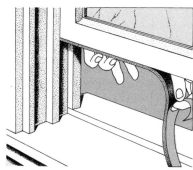

SELF-STICKING foam rubber weatherstrip installs easily, wears out fast.

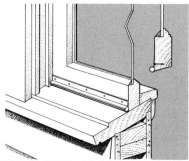

ROLLED VINYL strip is tough, easy to install, but highly visible.

TUBE CAULKING applied by gun does a quick job at all exterior joints.

Quick and easy renovations

■ Install a doorway at the top of your stairway and keep it closed in winter. It will prevent warm air from rising to the bedrooms (where less is needed), and cooled air upstairs from cascading down the stairwell into the living areas.

DOOR installed at top of a stairwell prevents heat from going upstairs.

■ Build a false dropped ceiling in the stairwell to prevent the warm air in downstairs rooms from collecting in the "heat trap" against the stairwell's two-story-high ceiling—where it does no one any good.

6'8" MIN.

FALSE CEILING over stairway eliminates a second-floor heat pocket.

■ Install doors to all rooms (including dining room, if possible), so that seldom-used areas can

UNNECESSARY WINDOWS should be removed and closed in permanently.

be closed off when unoccupied for reasonable lengths of time, and their heating units shut down.

■ Fill in unnecessary or unused windows—remove frame, insulate cavity and finish off the exterior and interior to match their respective wall surfaces.

■ If your house roof provides the proper exposure and area, or if there is open space exposed to the southern sun in winter, consider installing solar collectors to provide water-heating energy. A number of good systems are now available.

Add-on investments that can pay off

■ Install a clock thermostat. It will automatically turn down the heat when you retire and back up in the morning before you awake, to preset temperatures of your choice. It can pay back its cost (about $70 to $140) in fuel saving in one or two years. It should be installed professionally. Clock-timer units that trigger heating elements beneath the thermostat and "fool" it into not activating the furnace switch until a desired time, are cheaper ($30 to $50). Not all are dependable, however. Consult your heating specialist for the best system for you, and insist on a binding warranty.

■ Don't overlook similar clock timers to control central airconditioning, if you have it. It's far cheaper to re-cool the house than to let the unit run for hours when you're not there.

■ New flue-pipe heaters that fit in the metal flue section leading from your furnace to the chimney, pick up waste heat that normally would go up the stack and put it to use where you direct it. They're available through most large heating supply outlets. They can salvage up to five percent of heat that normally would be lost to the outdoors.

■ Automatic dampers that cut off the flue when the furnace kicks off prevent firebox heat from disappearing up the chimney. They can save a lot of heat, but must be installed by experienced professionals. Improper installation can back up exhaust gases into the furnace room. If you're about to buy a new furnace, however, consider getting one with a built-in automatic flue damper.

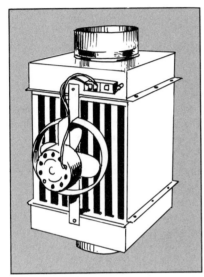

FLUE RADIATOR uses furnace-flue heat to warm a basement.

■ If you heat by electric furnace, it may be well worth your while to switch to a heat pump—an airconditioning-type device that draws heat from outside air (even when it's below zero) to warm the house, and reverses in summer to provide cooling. "Whole house" units cost about $2000 but can cut consumption of the energy required by an electric furnace as much as 40 percent.

■ A less expensive energy-saver is a new add-on heat pump The indoor coil fits on any type furnace to provide heat in winter and airconditioning in summer at considerable savings.

■ Another interesting energy-saver is a heat-recovery device the size of a large metropolitan telephone book. The unit, made hooks up to the hot-air exhaust of central airconditioners and uses the waste heat for hot water production.

■ Add a hot-water circulator to the fireplace to blow heat into the room that otherwise would be lost up the chimney.

■ If you have no fireplace damper, install glass doors in the opening. They'll not only serve as a damper when the fireplace is not in use, but can

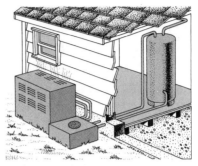

WASTE-HEAT device uses air-conditioner exhaust to heat water.

be shut to snuff out the fire when you retire or leave the house.

■ Put in an attic fan if you have none, and use it to bring outside air in through open windows on the shady side when it's 78° or less outdoors in summer. The airconditioner is wasting kilowatts when it's that cool outside. The fan uses far less energy.

■ Heat loss via the exterior entry door to your home can be substantial. Now it can be cut up to 16 percent by a new steel door with a honeycomb and foam core. The unit is designed to replace combination storm door and exterior wood door. It's made of 24-gauge steel and has an insulating value more than two times that of wood. DOE engineers used it with magnetized rubber weatherstip for a perfect seal.

■ Buy lamps with three-way switches and use the lowest wattage until you *need* more light. Better yet, install solid-state dimmers to control all of the lighting in the house. They can cut your lighting bill by up to one-third if properly used.

■ If you cook with gas, make your next stove one with piezoelectric ceramic starters instead of a pilot light. They'll save you the 30 percent extra gas that those pilot lights consume.

■ Make sure your next refrigerator has a power-saver switch to cut out the heating elements in the walls and doors (when not needed) to prevent condensation in humid weather. Also insist on manual defrost. Automatic uses more energy.

■ If your TV has an "instant on" feature, it's never really turned off. Use the "vacation" switch. And when you buy a new set, insist on one without the "instant on" gadget. It's costing you money.

■ Even if you have storm windows, a third pane of glass will cut the window heat loss in your home by a measured third. If you have central airconditioning, you may want to consider bronze glass, which cuts solar penetration in the summer.

Bring in fresh air without losing heat

■ HIGH FUEL PRICES have driven many homeowners to add more insulation, block out drafts, caulk cracks, install tighter windows and generally seal up their houses. The object of this exercise is to contain skyrocketing heating costs.

All of these procedures work, but now some homeowners are finding that they have done too good a job. Sure, they're saving on fuel bills, but they're also finding that odors linger not for

hours, but for days. Steam from the shower collects as condensate on windows. In short, the stale air inside the house remains inside instead of filtering out through the cracks.

The solution to this indoor air pollution problem is obvious—ventilate. But the difficulty is that you ventilate your expensive heat right out the window or open door.

There is a way to ventilate while retaining up

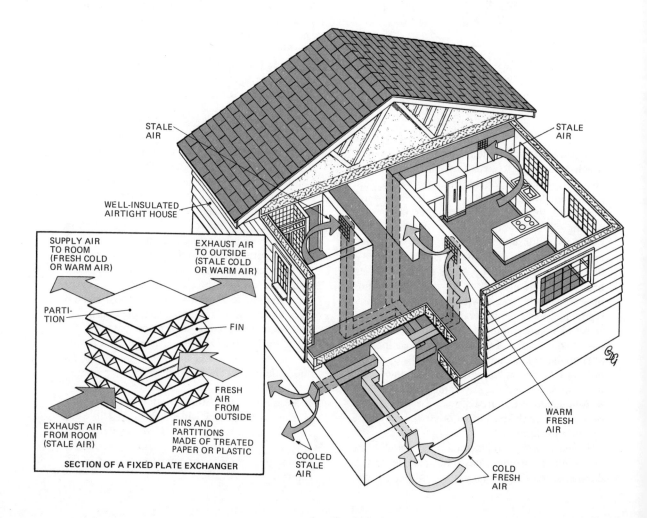

STALE AIR

STALE AIR

WELL-INSULATED AIRTIGHT HOUSE

SUPPLY AIR TO ROOM (FRESH COLD OR WARM AIR)

EXHAUST AIR TO OUTSIDE (STALE COLD OR WARM AIR)

PARTITION

FIN

EXHAUST AIR FROM ROOM (STALE AIR)

FRESH AIR FROM OUTSIDE

FINS AND PARTITIONS MADE OF TREATED PAPER OR PLASTIC

SECTION OF A FIXED PLATE EXCHANGER

COOLED STALE AIR

COLD FRESH AIR

WARM FRESH AIR

to 80 percent of the heat that would otherwise exit with the stale air. Air-to-air heat exchangers have been around on a commercial scale for more than a generation, but smaller models for residential use are new.

Air-to-air heat exchangers ventilate the whole house effectively, while handling the heat-loss problem efficiently. Efficiencies up to 80 percent save most of the heat which would otherwise be lost, while changing indoor air frequently enough to keep it both pleasant and healthy.

Latent heat

Some new air exchangers also transfer latent heat—the heat trapped in the water vapor held by the warm stale air. Condensing this water out of the stale air reclaims still more heat.

By exchanging both heat and vapor, the total energy content—called enthalpy—of the incoming clean air can be raised so it's from 70 to 80 percent of that in the outgoing stale air. This helps to maintain a comfortable temperature and humidity level inside the house.

When indoor relative humidity stays between 40 and 50 percent, your feeling of comfort prods you to turn down the thermostat by a few degrees—a step that makes a noticeable difference in fuel bills. It also keeps your furniture from drying out to the point where glue joints crack and walking on your rugs produces sufficient static electricity to cause shocks.

They work in summer, too

Air-to-air heat exchangers work equally well in summer to conserve your air-conditioned cool air. The principle is the same, but the direction of the heat and moisture exchange is reversed. Stale but cool indoor air (whether air-conditioned or not) is vented to the outside, taking the heat and excess moisture from the warmer incoming air with it. Enthalpy air-to-air heat exchangers also extract water vapor from the warmer incoming air, while cooling it to keep your house from the clammy feeling of excess humidity.

So much for the pluses. Even enthalpy air exchangers have their minuses. For one, unless your house is supertight, with an air change rate of 0.5 or less (one change every two hours), they do no good. In fact, a house that changes its air once an hour without help will only lose excessive amounts of heat no matter how efficient its air exchanger may be.

Freeze-ups may occur

The other problem with air exchangers, especially enthalpy models, is freeze-ups. Most are plagued by freeze-ups on the incoming airstream side when the outside temperature drops below 10° F. Ice forms, blocking up the openings. Most soon thaw from the warmth of outgoing air. Some have electric heaters, but these have their own energy expenses. Still, ice dams do lower the efficiency of some enthalpy air-to-air heat exchangers.

FIVE TYPICAL air exchangers go in basement or attic to ventilate superinsulated houses and reclaim heat from outgoing stale air. Designs (see text), warm incoming fresh air by passing it through a heat exchanger next to outgoing stale air. (3) is a rotary enthalpy design that conserves latent heat, resists freeze-up and rehumidifies.

Types of exchangers

Different types of air exchangers react differently to freeze-ups. Here's a quick rundown on the three main types of air-to-air heat exchangers: the fixed-plate "sensible" models, fixed-plate enthalpy designs, and rotary enthalpy exchangers.

Fixed-plate sensible heat exchangers get their name from your being able to sense the heat in the incoming air. They contain a series of nonporous separators mounted so that incoming and outgoing air travel through side-by-side channels; that way, the heat from one can warm the other without contaminating it. Heat is transferred through the separator. Two small fans pull in outside air and push out indoor air.

Shut down the fan

When a freeze-up occurs, a sensor can shut down the fan on the incoming side, or you've got to do so yourself. Then, outgoing warm air continues to transfer heat to the iced-up incoming channels, melting the ice. At about 20° F. outside, this is claimed to take only a minute or two. Down at 0° F. or below, it takes longer.

A very tight house collects vapor from cooking and bathing, which can steam up windows in cold weather. An air exchanger also removes this excess moisture quite rapidly, while bringing in only small amounts of humidity with the colder outside air in winter.

Humidifier may be required

Some air exchangers require a humidifier to replace the moisture removed with the stale air. This is a separate operation and is not incorporated in most models, so you may have to add a humidifier to the cost of an air exchanger. The need is most important on cold days.

Fixed-plate enthalpy exchangers work the same way as sensible models. The difference is in the separators. These are water absorbent, so they filter the moisture out of the stale air and pass it through to the clean incoming air. Thus, these models pass through both sensible and latent heat.

Fixed-plate models pass water vapor

By passing the water vapor through with the outside air, these models help to maintain the relative humidity balance in the house. However, they still lose some moisture to the outside, though markedly less than with a sensible design.

Rotary enthalpy exchangers are, at this writing, only available under the Econofresher name. In this design, a honeycombed wheel transfers heat and vapor from the outgoing warm air to the incoming cold air. Since the surface of the wheel is exposed to both cold and warm air, it appears to have overcome the freeze-up problem effectively. No single set of ducts is constantly exposed to freezing temperatures, so ice never builds up. Company literature claims frost-free operation down to 5° F. In summer, it's claimed to work well in keeping interiors cool and humidity balanced at a comfortable level.

Thermostatic roof vents

Another air exchange system relies on rising hot air for circulation and thermostatic controls in roof vents to minimize heat losses. It includes one or more roof vents to remove the stale air and manually controlled ceiling grilles to regulate airflow.

Each cap has a thermostat which opens air flaps when the temperature reaches 80° F. and closes them at 60° F. It has a built-in fuse to close the vanes and keep them closed in case of fire. By opening ceiling vents that feed inside air to the cap, you can keep the house comfortable and the humidity controlled.

With these vents closed in winter, the system is claimed to balance humidity and conserve energy. Fresh air enters the house through open downstairs windows or by natural infiltration if the house is not too tightly sealed. While this system does not heat the incoming air with the outgoing stale air, it requires no power for fans because it works by giving the hot, stale air a place to go when it rises.

Air exchanger problems

Three problems remain: how to select the right size unit, how to install it or have it installed, and where to find one.

Sizing depends on the volume of your house. A rough rule of thumb is to specify an air exchanger delivering 75 c.f.m. (cubic feet per minute) per 1,000 square feet of floor space.

You can arrive at a more precise estimation by using the calculations of ASHRAE (American Society of Heating, Refrigeration and Air Conditioning Engineers). They advise 40 c.f.m. for each bath or kitchen and 10 c.f.m. for each occupant. Then multiply the number of cubic feet in your home by the air-infiltration rate to get the air-change rate.

The Big Sucker

Air-infiltration rates were once determined by multiple instruments all over the house, but this expensive piecemeal method has been replaced by a machine which creates a vacuum and then measures how hard it has to work to do it. Called The Big Sucker (what else?), it was developed by a Texas utility about six years ago. Now, you can hire its services through local utilities and some air conditioning contractors. Once The Big Sucker gives you the air-infiltration rate per hour for your home—remember, adding insulation and sealing windows, doors or other air leaks changes it drastically—you can figure your air-change requirement.

In a supertight house, the average number of air changes per hour ranges from 0.2 to 0.3. To find out yours, multiply the air-infiltration rate per hour by the number of cubic feet in the house. Divide that number by 60 to get the number of c.f.m. of air your house changes naturally. Subtract this c.f.m. rate from your calculated need to get the exchanger capacity.

Installing an air exchanger

Installation calls for commonly used home-handyman skills and tools. Do not attempt to tie in with any existing ductwork if your house is heated by hot air, but make the air exchanger system separate and independent.

As the outgoing air gives up its heat to warm the fresh air coming in, moisture condenses. The drain line (which can be a plastic tube leading to the floor drain in the basement) gets rid of this water.

You will also have to work with ducting. Most air exchanger makers recommend flexible, insulated ducting with a vapor barrier. It must also fit the air exchanger fittings and should be available from the same source as the air exchanger.

Cellar and attic installations

Cellar installations support the air exchanger system on ceiling joists with straps. Attic installations can rest on ceiling joists. Some smaller models can be wall-mounted in a bathroom or kitchen like a sort of super exhaust fan.

Stale air can come from anywhere in the house, but the most effective systems take it from as high up in the room as possible. The area of the air intake should be open to the rest of the rooms. Plan to deliver fresh air to one room or several and exhaust it from another to minimize cross-contamination. There's no advantage in exhausting your fresh air or mixing it more than necessary with the outgoing stale air. Keep the outside air intake and the exhaust vent at least 6 feet apart to avoid cross contamination outside the house.

Build an energy-saving house

■ BUILDING A HOUSE that will conserve as much energy as possible isn't particularly difficult. Our ancestors knew how to do it, and so do we. But until recently, we did not consider it necessary to be concerned with how much energy we consumed—or how much we wasted through lack of planning. The energy crunch changed that outlook.

Though a new house with energy-conservation features generally costs more than one without them, your initial cash outlay—and more—will be returned in the form of savings on heating bills. For example, once the house has been closed in, you can provide insulation in exterior walls only by chopping holes in the walls around the house perimeter and blowing in the material. The time, therefore, to think of saving energy is in the planning stage.

In broad terms, there are five planning steps you can take to save as much energy as possible:

1. Position house on the site with regard to exposure and all the elements.
2. Design the home for efficient energy use.
3. Select materials and workmanship that will conserve energy.
4. Plan the use of insulation.
5. Get top efficiency from appliances, mechanical equipment and fireplaces.

Position your house with care

The basic idea is to use the natural terrain to protect the house from the elements. For example, can your house be built in a valley instead of on top of a hill? Can you locate it on the protected side of a hill or on the sunny side of a slope? Remember, you can obtain some insulation by building partly *into* a hillside.

And don't make the mistake of arbitrarily clearing all rocks and vegetation from the site. Look for this fault particularly if buying a contractor-built or vacation community home. Many builders and developers find it cheaper to build if just about all trees are knocked down and the land is leveled.

Allow for sun and wind

Always keep sun and wind in mind when locating your house on a site. In cold-weather areas, winter winds usually come from the North, so it makes sense to face the walls with maximum insulation and minimum glass area that way. If the house design and property layout permit, the shortest wall should face north.

In much of today's architecture, especially in leisure-home designs, large areas of glassed walls seem almost mandatory. By siting your house so the glass walls face south, the low winter sun will shine into them during most of the daylight hours and ease the load on the heating system. In warmer areas, where cooling is of primary concern, the glass areas should also face south. With properly designed overhangs (often called "eyebrows"), little or no sun comes in during the summer when the sun is high. By contrast, if these windows are on the east or west sides, they pick up heat almost half the day, thus putting a burden on the house cooling system.

You can get protection as well as beauty from landscaping, too. A row of evergreens planted to the north or northwest of a house can be an effective wind barrier.

Tall deciduous trees should be retained or planted to the south, west or east of the house to provide cooling shade in the summer. In winter, after the leaves have fallen, these trees do not block the roof and walls from the warming rays of the sun.

Design a functional house

Use plain common sense when picking your house—don't be guided by esthetics alone. If you

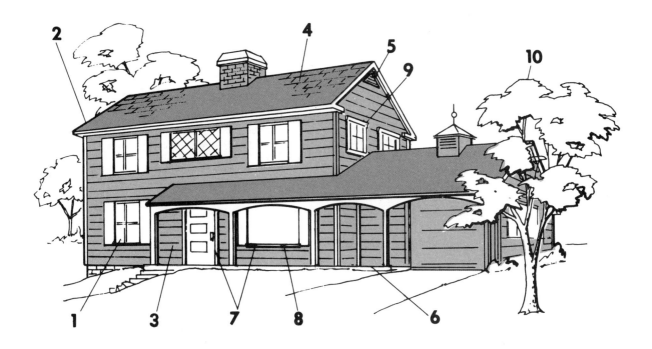

Here are 10 things you can do to help keep fuel bills down

1. Use double-glazed windows throughout to reduce heat transmission up to 50 percent.

2. When choosing a house style, favor multilevel designs over ranch homes. Their proportionately smaller roof areas for a given amount of space cut down heat loss.

3. Insulate exposed walls with material having an R-value at least 11 (3½-in. mineral wool batts or equivalent); ceilings with material having an R-value at least 19 (6 in. thick).

4. Use light-colored shingles on the roof to reflect sunlight and thus assist cooling equipment.

5. Adequately ventilate attic to lessen solar heat gain.

6. Use a minimum of 1-in.-thick perimeter insulation for on-grade slabs and footings.

7. Accept only tight installations of windows and doors. Cracks existing between frames and rough openings should be packed with insulation and sealed with an appropriate vapor-barrier material.

8. Caulk around all joints between windows, doors and siding with a high-quality latex or butyl caulk compound.

9. In extra-cold climates, use storm windows. When tightly fitted, they can reduce infiltration of air by 30 to 50 percent.

10. Preserve as many trees as possible for reasons explained in the text.

question your knowledge in this area, an architect should be consulted.

First, make sure your house is designed for the climate it will be exposed to. For example, a house with a sprawling layout and large areas of glass walls might suit the climate perfectly in the southwest United States. But park the same house in the northern reaches of Maine, and it becomes an energy-guzzling monster to heat.

The house should be practical to heat and cool. The design feature to key in on is the ratio of roof area to floor area (see sketch): The lower the ratio, the easier it will be to heat or cool the house. Though the drawing shows that a round house is most efficient in this regard, that shape is difficult to build and live in. Next best is a square house; after that in decreasing efficiency, the rectangular, L, H and T shapes.

In colder climates, a two-story house makes good sense. Since most heat is lost through the roof, a two-story house saves money because it has a lower proportion of roof to floor area. You can save as much as 15 percent in fuel consumption by having living areas on two levels instead

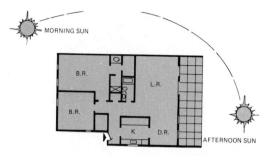

CONSIDER YOUR floor plan: Keep common (or active) living space confined to one part of the house and sleeping (or inactive) rooms in another for zoned heating and cooling. Active rooms may be warmed by facing them toward the afternoon sun.

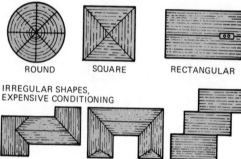

GOOD SHAPE, EASY CONDITIONING

ROUND SQUARE RECTANGULAR

IRREGULAR SHAPES, EXPENSIVE CONDITIONING

THE KEY to efficient heating and cooling is the ratio of roof to floor areas—the less roof area, the better. A two-level house has a lower proportion of roof to floor area and can save up to 15 percent on fuel.

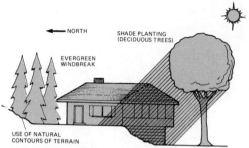

LANDSCAPING SHOULD protect your property as well as beautify it. A row of evergreens north of your house breaks the wind, while deciduous trees on the other sides provide shade in the summer and allow warming sunlight through in the winter when they are bare. Use of terrain is also helpful.

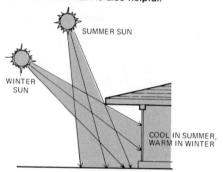

CORRECTLY DESIGNED roof overhangs shield walls from the higher summer sun, yet expose the same walls to the winter sun which is at a lower angle. An attached porch, carport or patio roof also serves to protect the walls.

of sprawled out on one level.

Give careful attention also to your floor plan. Grouping common living space in one part of the house and sleeping quarters in another facilitates zoned heating and cooling (dual thermostats, one for each area) and allows the closing off of a section when not in use. If possible, family rooms, kitchens and dining rooms should face south and west so they are warmed by the afternoon sun. Bedrooms should be oriented to the morning sun so they can be cooled easily for comfortable sleeping.

Well-planned ventilation can reduce the need for home cooling. In fact, many architects agree that in some regions, airconditioning is totally unnecessary if the house is properly ventilated. Along these lines, a courtyard or atrium (enclosed or open) can be used to create better ventilation; even though an atrium adds wall area, it may cut the cooling load.

Don't automatically opt for large expanses of glass—the major cause of heat loss. Windows should be positioned and located with more than a view in mind. Too often, they are included for esthetic reasons only and are not operable for ventilation. Often, when the cooling system is spinning the meter at dizzying speed, the house could be cooled by merely opening and closing the right windows.

High ceilings waste heat

Cathedral ceilings are dramatic. But be aware that such ceilings can bring with them serious heating problems. Energy is wasted in conditioning a large volume of air in high unused spaces. And, since warm air rises, it is especially difficult to heat high-ceilinged rooms.

Old architectural standbys can still save a lot of energy. Attached porches, carports and decking can also protect windows and doors from the direct rays of the sun if they are carefully laid out. If your architectural design allows, consider using operable shutters over windows to screen out direct rays of the sun and cold wind blasts.

When you compromise function, you're almost certain to compromise good design.

Coal makes a comeback

EMPTYING ASH PAN assures efficiency. Coal requires more attention than gas or liquid fuels, but less than wood.

■ MORE THAN 300,000 coal stoves were sold in one recent year, according to the Department of Energy. Coal distributors were swamped with orders from eager homeowners.

Assisting the central heating system with a space heater can save lots of money. Highly efficient coal is a natural choice of fuels for this purpose.

Bituminous and anthracite are the two major kinds of coal. Anthracite, in the size of "pea" or "nut," is the coal used in most space heaters and new home furnaces. It is celebrated for its high efficiency, low sulfur content and production of little ash and practically no smoke. Because anthracite is harder than bituminous coal, it is also relatively clean to handle. It was the soft, crumbly, bituminous coal used in home furnaces in the '40s (now largely used in industry) that gave coal its "dirty" reputation.

Availability of coal

One of coal's most attractive features is the amount buried under our feet, rather than in the sands of some Arabian desert. Industrial engineers estimate that the nation's coal reserves are so abundant they will last for centuries.

It is comforting to know that the fuel is domestically abundant, but the question of cost and economy is nevertheless complicated.

Coal is both mined and transported by labor-intensive industries. This means that supply and price can be affected by strikes and the state of the nation's economy.

Also, 90 percent of all anthracite coal is located in a small area of northeastern Pennsylvania. Therefore, transportation costs are an important factor for this kind of coal.

One expert we contacted suggested this rule of thumb: Given the present price and wage structure in the industry, if you are located more than 700 miles from the mine, one of the other fuels is probably a better deal for your fuel dollar.

Called "coking," burning coal actually becomes liquefied as it gives up its volatile compounds in the combustion process. The combustion area may be very small, but the heat is intense, reaching temperatures in excess of 2,200 ° F.

Coal requires its primary source of air (80 percent) to come up through the bed from below, while the other 20 percent must come in over the top of the fire. As it burns, it produces a very fine ash which remains in the combustion area until the bed is shaken very gently to allow this ash to sift through the coals, the grate, and into the ash pan below. This is a delicate feature of coal, for improper shaking can disturb the bed so much that the flame is extinguished. In addition, if disturbed too much, ash may become mixed with the liquefying coal and form "clinkers." Clinkers look like volcanic rock and are a nuisance. They stick to grates and other stove parts and waste fuel.

Our knowledge of coking allows us to set some requirements for the well-designed stove. One essential feature is some form of baffle to help ab-

BASIC STOVE

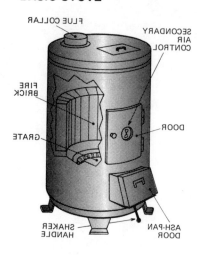

INTERNAL HOPPER

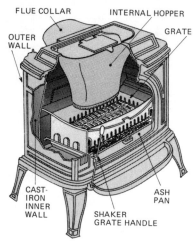

AUTOMATIC STOKER

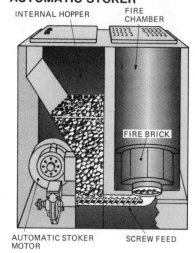

BECAUSE FUEL is hand-fed into fire chamber in simple stoves, these designs require most attention.

CONVENIENT internal hoppers are popular for space heaters. A double-walled stove can hold day's fuel supply.

IN THE MOST convenient space heaters (not typical), and furnaces, an automatic screw feeds coal.

sorb and disperse the intense heat evenly in the immediate area of combustion. Most stove manufacturers insist this requirement is best met by a fire-chamber lining of firebrick—very much like that used in industrial ceramic kilns. The immediate and apparent drawback is that any such stove is going to be very heavy. Some manufac-

turers claim that a lighter, double-wall stove with a cast-iron interior helps to do the same thing— air passing between the walls draws heat from the hot spot. In either case, the heat must be drawn out efficiently or it will begin to melt the interior of the stove.

Because of the primary and secondary air re-

THIS FIREBRICK-LINED stove includes all features of basic design: Primary air control is usually built into ash-pan door. Ceramic-glass doors allow a view of the glowing coals.

INTERNAL HOPPER model has ceramic face panels to distribute heat.

IN APPEARANCE, this furnace boiler is typical of larger coal burners, whether fed by hand (like this one) or fed automatically. Versatility of coal furnaces produces a wide price range.

MANY STOVE MAKERS also offer fireplace insert stoves. Some inserts burn cannel coal brightly.

quirements of coal, the grate design is also important. Usually composed of one stationary part and one movable part, it must allow for gentle shaking of the entire bed at once and be designed to support the coal, yet allow the unimpeded passage of primary air up through the bed.

Airtight construction is a must for burning coal efficiently. A well-designed stove will have controls for primary and secondary air supplies.

Basic stoves come in a multitude of sizes and shapes. Depending on decorative features, prices can vary widely. The main drawback of the simple stove is that it must be stoked regularly.

For convenience, the most popular coal stove has an internal hopper which can allow up to 1½ days' supply of coal to be fed to the stove at a time. Most internal hoppers work on a gravity-feed principle. As the coal burns, the bed settles; this allows more coal to descend from the hopper into the fire chamber. Most internal hopper stoves have double-walled construction instead of a firebrick lining.

A few space heaters have not only an internal hopper, but also a thermostatically controlled stoker system which feeds the coal to the burning chamber by means of a screw mechanism. Be-

cause of the machinery and storage size of the hopper, this design is usually used for hot-water heaters and central-heating furnaces. One drawback of automatic stokers is that they produce an intermittent disturbing, crunching noise when the screw-feed is working.

One of the great myths about wood stoves is now apparent: You cannot burn coal in a wood stove without probable damage from intense heat, unless the firebox and grates are designed to handle both fuels.

Stove makers are under great pressure to provide versatile stoves that can burn a variety of fuels. But the challenge of producing an efficient coal and wood stove is considerable, because of the marked differences in the ways these fuels burn. The fact is, a stove that will burn both will burn neither efficiently.

While efficiency is the key word in coal stoves, be wary of any maker claiming an efficiency greater than 70 percent. All fuels have their limits, regardless of burner design.

Tips on burning coal

■ The kindling temperature of coal is around 800° F. This means a kindling fire of wood is necessary to get the coals started.

■ If smoking occurs during the fire, there is probably something amiss in the flue. This is the most common problem with coal stoves.

■ Make sure that the size coal specified by your stove is available. Don't burn other sizes or kinds of coal or your grate won't work properly.

■ Because it is a small industry, there is less flexibility in delivery and supply systems of anthracite coal. Order early.

■ Develop patterns of checking your coal stove regularly. Even the automatic stokers require ash removal by hand on a regular basis.

■ Never disturb the bed of burning coals with a poker, as used to be the practice with old potbellies burning bituminous. This disturbance will produce clinkers and defeat the purpose of the well-designed grate.

■ Finally, remember to follow the maker's instructions carefully to get maximum stove performance from this highly efficient fuel. Burning coal, however, does require a certain modification of your lifestyle. Unlike gas or liquid fuel, which you may never even see, coal is handled and the stove must be tended. Rather than thinking this inconvenient, some homeowners seem to feel that they want to be closer to the basic household necessities.

Caulking basics

■ THE HIGH PRICE of fuel is reason enough to seal your house tightly with caulk to keep out costly—and chilly—blasts of winter air. But there are other reasons for maintaining a good, periodic caulking program. A properly sealed home is protected from unnecessary damage—inside and out—due to the effects of weather extremes, wind, dirt and moisture. And caulking will do much to eliminate unsightly paint failures such as mildew and peeling.

A common mistake is to think that all caulk materials are alike. Believing that, many home-owners will buy a tube of caulking that sells for $1 or less—after spending $10 or more per gallon to repaint their homes.

A homeowner should be familiar with three types of caulk. Oil base is the cheapest. But, more often than not, the other types will do the job better. Here's the rule to follow when choosing caulk: Always pick the one best suited to the job at hand. The chart below will help you do just that.

What kind of caulk should you use?

Type	Advantages	Disadvantages
Oil base	Low cost.	Short use-life. Requires recaulking each year. Can't be painted for 24 hours. Flexibility is limited. Has minimal allowance for movement. Has poor adhesion to many surfaces.
Butyl	Long life. Good to excellent adhesion to most surfaces. Good flexibility at most temperatures.	Solvent required for cleanup. Composition tends to be stringy. Also tends to pick up dirt.
Acrylic latex	Long life. Good to excellent adhesion to most surfaces. Requires only 30 minutes setup time before painting. Easy to handle. Good weathering characteristics. Water and soap used for cleanup.	Should not be subjected to rain immediately after application.

STOP COSTLY DRAFTS by caulking joints where siding meets door casings. Clean out old caulk, and make certain the surfaces are clean and free of all dust. Apply a bead, holding the caulk gun at a 45° angle to the surface. Your best bet: *acrylic-latex caulk.*

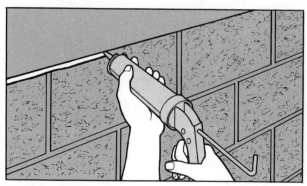

SEAL OPEN JOINTS between house siding and foundation. If crack is more than ½ in. deep, push in urethane filler before you begin caulking. Squeeze caulk from the tube and force it into crack with a putty knife. *Use butyl or acrylic-latex caulk.*

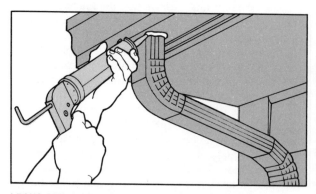

LEAKS APPEARING at rusted drop outlets where downspouts join gutters can be stopped by caulking. For good adhesion, be sure surface is completely dry and free of rust. After applying caulk, tool bead flat with a putty knife. *Use butyl caulk.*

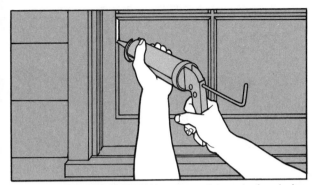

CAULKING MATERIAL makes quick work of reglazing chores. Remove all loose chips, dust off and apply caulk to the glass-wood joint. Spread the caulk with a putty knife; periodically dip the knife in water to make the spreading easier. *Use acrylic latex caulk.*

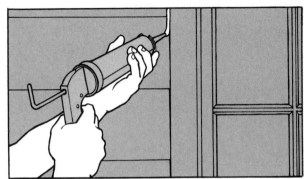

PAINT FAILURES are usually due to moisture entering siding material at the end grain; thus, joints at siding/window-casings should be caulked. Other spots to caulk: Where two lengths of siding butt each other and at the corners. *Use acrylic latex caulk.*

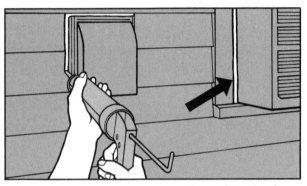

CRACKS AROUND wall caps (for ventilators) and airconditioners should be sealed with a bead of caulking between the siding and the fixture. If desired, cap can be loosened and then reset in bed of caulk. *Use acrylic latex or butyl caulk* for this job.

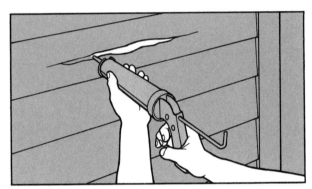

UNSIGHTLY CRACKS or nailholes in siding can be filled quickly by forcing caulk into the crevice, then feathering the edges smooth. After removing any excess caulk, the material can then be painted to match the rest of the siding. *Use acrylic-latex caulk.*

TO PREVENT WATER from seeping into your home, seal every plumbing fixture (hose bibb shown) and electrical outlet. Force the caulk into the joint around fixture. If necessary, first stuff in urethane or some other nonstaining filler. *Use butyl or acrylic latex caulk.*

LOOSE FLASHING around chimneys can be a source of continual water leakage into the house. To close this gap, run a bead of caulking into the seam between the flashing and shingles. If necessary, also caulk between flashing and chimney. *Use butyl caulk.*

Insulation installation

■ THERE ARE FOUR good reasons why you should insist on adequate insulation when buying a new home or remodeling an existing one. *First:* The cost of heating and cooling in any given locale is proportional to the heat-loss/gain factor of the dwelling. You pay for heat and cooling that escapes through those walls. *Sec-* *ond:* Comfort. Insulation, installed properly, eliminates drafts and increases comfort appreciably and measurably (by the thermostat). *Third:* Acoustical privacy, particularly important if you own a multiple dwelling. Insulation in wall and floor cavities helps to reduce airborne noises, such as loud voices, and impact sounds, such as heavy footsteps. And *fourth:* A reason seldom considered when insulation is being discussed—its effectiveness as a fire barrier. Mineral-wool insulation is noncombustible; when it fills a wall cavity, it acts as a deterrent to the vertical spread of fire. In fact, if the walls in new construction are filled with insulation, then fire-blocking (fire stops) can be eliminated. What you will thus save on labor and materials can be deducted from your insulation cost.

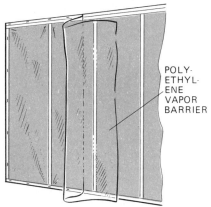

WHEN YOU USE pressure-fit blankets without a vapor barrier, wedge them into place and then cover the wall with 2-mil-thick polyethylene vapor barrier stapled to the top and bottom plates. Unroll the sheet to cover the entire wall area, including window and door openings, then cut to length. Staple to end studs, cut out openings and staple around openings.

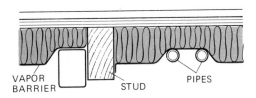

IF OBSTRUCTIONS—ducts, pipes and the like—are located in your wall cavities, push insulation behind (to the cold side in winter) those pipes before stapling. Or you can pack the space with loose insulation or cut a piece of blanket insulation to fit the space. If you do pack the space with loose insulation, make certain you cover it with 2-mil polyethylene.

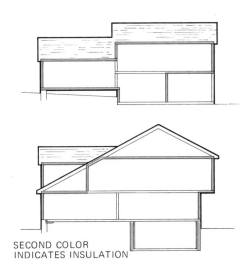

SECOND COLOR INDICATES INSULATION

EFFECTIVE LOCATIONS for insulation are indicated by colored lines in the drawing above. To assure that your home is free of moisture problems, remember that you must install adequate vapor barriers. If you use one of the types of insulation that comes without a vapor barrier, install polyethylene, as described at right. The vapor barrier is always installed between the insulation and interior of the home.

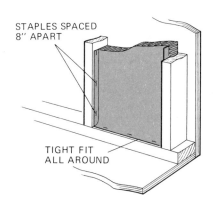

BLANKETS should be pushed into stud spaces so they touch siding or sheathing. Working from the top down, space the staples about 8 in. apart, pulling flanges to fit snugly over studs. Cut the blanket end slightly overlength and staple through the vapor barrier to the plates by compressing the insulation.

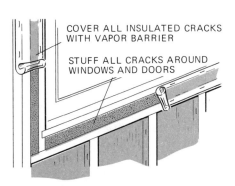

USE SCRAPS of insulation to stuff into small spaces between rough framing and door and window heads, jambs and sills. You can fill even the narrowest cracks by using a putty knife to force the pieces of insulation in until the crack is filled. Staple scraps of the insulation vapor barrier, or polyethylene, in place to cover those small stuffed spaces.

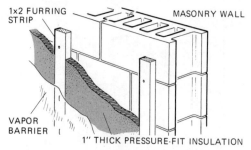

EASIEST WAY TO INSULATE MASONRY WALLS is to space nominal 1x2 furring strips 16 in. on center with nominal 1-in. pressure-fit masonry-wall insulation between strips. Cover with polyethylene vapor barrier. If you prefer 2x2 furring, and use R-7 insulation (with vapor barrier), strips can be spaced 24 in. o.c. This insulation backs up wall panels.

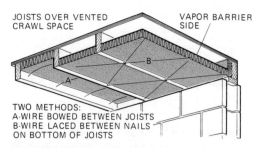

FLOOR OVER VENTED CRAWL SPACE can be insulated if insulating material is held between joists, using either of these methods: (A) By using heavy-gauge wires pointed at both ends, made especially for this purpose. Just bow wires and wedge them underneath insulation between joists. (B) By lacing wires between nails placed in bottom of joists.

HEADER JOIST should be covered with insulation, too. You can do it by wedging oversize pieces of blanket insulation between joists behind the band of header joists and stapling edges to the joists. Or, when you are using insulation at the bottom of joists, you can insulate the header joist by "folding" the end of the blanket 90°, pushing it back against the header and then driving in a few staples.

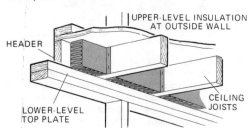

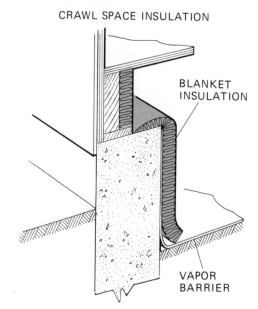

FLOOR OVER UNVENTED CRAWL SPACE usually can be insulated more economically as shown above than by methods given at left for floor over vented crawl space. Spread the vapor barrier over ground in crawl space, let it turn up onto the walls and hold it there with tape. Then place one edge of the blanket insulation on top of the foundation wall and let it drape over and against the inside of the wall. The vapor barrier must face inward.

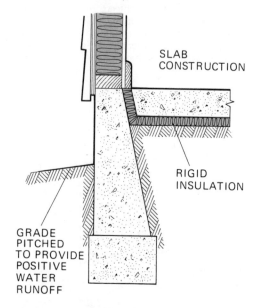

SLAB-FOUNDATION HOMES should always be insulated. The correct way is to lay a 6-mil polyethylene vapor barrier over tamped gravel and use rigid insulation between barrier and slab. The same material should also be used for perimeter insulation, installed as shown. For any insulating job, don't scrimp on quality or thickness. The material is relatively inexpensive and you will recoup its cost in the form of heating and cooling savings.

Heat thieves in your home

■ FOR THIS ARTICLE, we asked five engineers at the Energy Research and Development Administration (ERDA), now part of the Department of Energy (DOE), to spell out the 10 most common heat-loss areas. You're probably familiar with the big losers like an uninsulated attic and uncaulked openings around windows and doors. But some thieves on DOE's "10 most-wanted" list may surprise you.

In each category DOE engineers estimated a range of dollar savings you can get by following our heat-saving plans. The figures are based on an average, 1750-square-foot house in a northern state and were current at the time this was written and may be even greater now.

Savings will vary. You'll get high-range savings in categories where your house is totally deficient and low-range savings where you're improving protection you already have, like adding insulation in your attic. It's not too late to start saving your winter fuel dollars—they'll come in handy for next summer's vacation!

1 Duct/pipe insulation

Sheet-metal heat ducts and copper hot-water supply pipes are the two most common types of heat supply. Unfortunately, both act as heat exchangers as well as suppliers. For example, if a duct pipe runs through an unheated area like a crawl space, a substantial amount of heat will be lost through walls of the duct before it reaches the register. DOE investigators have found extreme cases in contemporary houses with cantilevered upper stories, where hot-air ducts were actually exposed to the weather. One engineer noted: "They lose more heat to the outside air

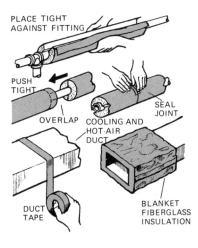

PLACE TIGHT AGAINST FITTING

PUSH TIGHT

OVERLAP

COOLING AND HOT-AIR DUCT

SEAL JOINT

DUCT TAPE

BLANKET FIBERGLASS INSULATION

than they convey to the rooms they were installed to serve."

Note: The DOE engineers concede that exposed ducting and piping in full basements and crawl spaces help warm the ground floor and, in some cases, serve to heat usable basement areas. If this reasoning is followed, they suggest that the basement itself should be insulated as specified under section 10 of this report.

2 Storm windows and doors

Glass acts as a heat exchanger to the outdoors. Single panes in a home with about 18 windows and two glass-lighted doors can lose more than 20 percent of your heat during an average northern winter. This is a "heat leak" any do-it-yourselfer can plug easily. While triple-track combination storm-and-screen sash is convenient and efficient, it costs $30 and up per window, installed. Dead air space is what counts. You can now buy transparent plastic sash in a kit. The 1/16-inch polyethylene sheet fits a vinyl mounting frame with pressure-sensitive tape on one side that seals it to the *inside* of the window casing—no ladder acrobatics necessary. The frame, white but paintable to match your color scheme if desired, remains permanently attached to the window. The clear plastic sheet is removable by unsnapping the lip of the vinyl frame—a fingertip operation. The unit comes for basic window sizes, priced accordingly.

3 Maximum attic insulation

One of the most effective ways to cut fuel costs is to insulate your attic. While most homes today have *some* insulation in the overhead, few are equipped with enough, say the experts. DOE authorities now recommend blanket or batt-type insulation rated R-30 for oil or gas-heated homes in cold winter zones. That's about 10 inches, made up in two layers since batts don't come that thick. Electrically heated homes in cold climes call for R-38 (about 12 inches). Heat engineers point out that if you already have six inches or more, additional thicknesses won't pay off in dollar savings over a reasonable length of time, except in the coldest areas or if you have electric heat. There are three basic systems for insulating attics:

■ **Unfinished, unfloored.** Batts can be layered one atop the other between joists, extending above them as needed.

■ **Unfinished, floored** (with no insulation beneath the boards). Remove the floor, lay batts between and to full depth of joists, and replace floor. If more insulation is needed for maximum protection, staple batts between the rafters as well.

■ **Finished attics.** Lay batts between joists above the ceilings of the finished rooms (you may have to cut a ceiling trapdoor to do this). Staple additional batts between the outer roof rafters (see sketch) beyond the knee walls of the rooms. Engineers also recommend that the attic gable-end walls in these triangular spaces also be insulated between studs.

What about sidewall insulation throughout the house? DOE experts disagree with some other agencies on retrofitting existing buildings. Their studies have shown that injection of wall insulation must be done commercially; that it is far too expensive for dollar payback in a reasonable time and usually proves inadequate.

An energy agency in Minnesota foam-insulated a test wall and later removed interior panels to check the coverage. "Three were voids all over the place," reports a DOE scientist. "Wire cables, electric boxes, fire stops and 'cats' set up barriers that completely blocked the foaming urethane as it tried to spread out."

4 Caulking and weatherstripping

In many homes, DOE investigators found that up to 70 percent of heat loss was due to infiltration of outside air coming through window and door casings and building sills. Wherever different materials or parts of a building join, caulking should be applied and regularly renewed. Tube cartridges and a gun are the basic tools, and anyone can do the job. Places to check and caulk if needed:

But attics are another matter. Even if yours *is* insulated, check to see how much you have. If another 4 to 6 inches would bring you up to R-22 or R-30 rating, the investment will pay off if you install it yourself.

■ All joints between door and window frames and siding.

■ Along bottom edge of siding where it laps the foundation wall, as well as inside the basement where the sill rests on the foundation.

■ Outside water faucet plates and other penetrations of the outside walls.

■ Joints between wing extensions, porches and main body of the house.

■ Where outside chimney or other masonry joins the house wall.

Large gaps, often found between foundation wall and back of siding, should be packed with oakum, caulking cotton or similar filler before caulking is applied. Most cartridge-type caulks today will do an adequate job. Butyl and silicone types will stay resilient and resist cracking.

Weatherstripping windows and doors—an obvious heat-leak stopper—can be done by amateurs nowadays, using any of the wide variety of materials.

■ **Foam-rubber** stripping backed with adhesive is easiest to install, and least expensive. Applied against door jambs it's good for a year or two but should be replaced when worn. It can't be used on double-hung sash except as a top and bottom seal, since it won't stand up under friction of the sliding sections.

■ **Rolled vinyl,** tacked to door jambs and window frames of any type, also is simple to install and provides a long-lasting seal. The only disadvantage is its visibility. On double-hung windows the "roll" should press lightly against the wood frame of the sash at sides, bottom and top. A strip nailed to the underside of the top sash laps and seals the joint between upper and lower window halves. On casement windows the strips are tacked so the window compresses the "roll" when shut.

■ **Thin spring metal** makes a highly durable seal for doors and most types of window, and is invisible when properly installed. It can be handled by do-it-yourselfers, but is difficult and somewhat exacting; doors are much easier than double-hung windows. The strips must be installed by opening the sash and sliding the side strips into the channel behind the sash frame, where it is tacked under the sash cords. Full-width strips are fastened to the underside of the bottom rail on the lower sash, and top of the upper sash top rail, and a full-width strip goes on the inside of the bottom rail of the top sash, with nailheads hammered flush so the window will close easily.

■ **Metal J-strips** for doors and casement windows call for critical alignment, but provide durability and an excellent seal.

Door-bottom drafts can be stopped with simple "sweeps" that fasten to the outside of the bottom rail, or "vinyl bulb" thresholds, which require door renoval and fitting. Interlocking metal thresholds are even more fussy, and require careful and accurate alignment.

5 Insulate water heater

You can save from $5 to $45 on this facility just by cutting down the water temperature. Normally, 120° F. is plenty hot. Dishwashers without heating elements, however, demand a 140° supply, but anything above that is wasted and can shorten the life of a glass-lined heater as well. The heat experts have determined that an additional 5 to 8 percent of water-heater energy can be saved by wrapping the unit in an outside layer of insulation. Johns-Manville now has insulation kits that are designed especially for either electric or gas water heaters. DOE engineers warn that if you wrap your gas heater, take care not to block air vents, and the top of the tank should be left uncovered.

The small cost of doing this job will pay for itself in less than a year. Another saver: drain a gallon of water from the bottom of the tank each year. Sediment that settles in the bottom insulates the water from the heating element.

6 Upgrade the furnace

According to DOE, most of what can be done about a furnace should be handled by professionals. To check the efficiency of your setup, the amount of "fuel-in" and "energy-out" must be measured, as must the chemical content of the exhaust. Fuel suppliers may have the instruments to do this. An inefficient furnace will show low carbon dioxide and high temperature in the stack. An efficient oil furnace should run above 14 percent CO_2, and less than 450° F. stack temperature. Gas should run the same for CO_2, but under 330°. Besides the usual filter changes (in forced hot-air systems), air bleeding (in hot-water systems), cleaning and adjustments, several other things can be done to enhance performance of any heating system:

■ **Steam and hot water.** Installation of a "baffle" in the firebox will spread the flame to the sidewalls and heat the medium more quickly. Heat engineers caution that installation should be made by specialists, since exhaust gases are slowed by the device, and it may create a hazard unless properly fitted.

■ **Forced hot air.** Up to 10 percent of a home's total heat loss may result from faulty cyclic operation of the furnace. This can be decreased by setting the fan at five degrees above the thermostat setting, and turn it on as near above that setting as the switch permits.

The old controversy over whether it's better to feed the furnace combustion chamber with preheated inside air, or introduce cold air from outdoors, is settled, according to DOE. An enclosed duct system bringing cold air directly from outside to the furnace has proven to be the most efficient system. One engineer explained, "A furnace operating on inside air pulls cold air into the house all the time and a significant amount of the warm air it uses is shot up the chimney."

Small-diameter ducts (usually about 4 inches) bringing outside air to the variable draft fan on oil furnaces, for example, will keep the furnace running cleaner and more efficiently.

7 Flue-pipe retrofits

A distressing part of any fossil-fueled furnace is that a significant percentage of the heat it produces goes up the flue. Some interesting new devices, however, now recapture some of that lost energy. A typical device is the heat pipe.

■ **Heat pipe.** This compact heat exchanger can be attached to either a vertical or horizontal flue pipe run. What it does is intercept the waste heat on its way to the chimney, extract it from the gases and redirect it to wherever it's wanted—to warm the basement, a particular upstairs room via extra duct, or it can be fed into the house duct system. A danger, scientists point out, is that removing too much heat from exhaust gases can decrease their buoyancy and result in a reverse flow. Hence, heat pipes, too should be installed by specialists, says DOE.

Lack of proper draft in the chimney, besides producing toxic gas in the house, could also ruin the furnace.

8 Fireplace damper

No builder today would install a fireplace without a damper, but many that are installed fit poorly and don't close snugly. In many old houses, the fireplace chimney is wide open, drawing warm air to the outdoors as effectively as an open window.

While the installation of an effective damper in an existing fireplace is an expensive business, extremely attractive glass fronts for fireplaces are readily available. The glass doors can be opened when a fire is blazing, and closed to seal off the entire opening when the hearth is not in use. Vents across the bottom can be opened to provide a draft if you like your fire behind glass. The units run about $125 and up, depending on quality and size of opening. They can save up to 6 percent of the annual heat you put into your house, and will pay for themselves in about two years with the protection that they provide.

9 Thermostat controls

Slide-rule wizards have calculated that if everyone in the country set back his thermostat about 10° at bedtime and turned it up at about 5 a.m., the result would be a saving of about 4 percent of the country's total yearly fuel consumption. For each homeowner it would amount to about 10 percent annual saving in the North; 30 percent in the South. Well, now a number of devices on the market will do the work for you.

■ **Clock thermostat.** Several versions are being produced by well-known companies, and most heating supply outlets carry them. They range from about $40 to $150. You set them to drop a given number of degrees at 10:00 or 11:00 p.m., and move up to the desired room temperature again in time for your morning shower.

■ **Clock-triggered resistor.** This device does the same job by fooling the thermostat into shutting down the furnace at night and returning it to normal operation before you wake up. Some four manufacturers currently are producing them. They cost from $10 to $30 and are easy to install. The timer unit is simply plugged into a nearby outlet and the unit is mounted directly below your thermostat. Small amounts of electricity cause heat to flow from the resistor at the top of the unit to the temperature sensing controls of the thermostat. The built-in 24-hour timer lets you set the off-on cycle to your convenience.

10 Basement insulation

If you've insulated heating ducts or heat-system pipes in your basement or crawl space, it is almost essential to insulate the house foundation walls to protect water pipes and to make the basement livable. In accessible crawl spaces, batts are run between each floor joist, over the sill, down the wall and across three or four feet of the earth floor inside the space. In full basements, 2x3 framing (with sill and plate) is built on two-foot centers, against the foundation with insulation batts run between. The batts need only extend down the wall as far as the frost line for your location. This structure then can be covered with dry-wall panels to accommodate the use to which the space will be put. In both foundation types, a vapor-barrier sheet should be laid against the concrete surface just beneath the insulation.

Energy saving tips

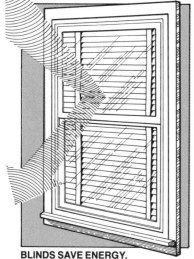

BLINDS SAVE ENERGY.
Blinds help keep out undesirable solar radiation in summer, yet let in cool breezes. In winter, they can let in solar radiation and diffuse sunlight to give natural lighting.

FREEZING NEWSPAPERS.
As you empty your freezer, or when you buy a new one, fill the empty sections with newspaper. The paper displaces air space with solid, cold-retaining material so your freezer won't run as often. In a power outage, a filled freezer keeps food frozen longer than a half-filled one.

WEATHERSTRIPPING

SEALED MAIL FLAP. Make certain that your mail slot flap closes tightly after mail has been delivered. Weatherstrip around the flap if necessary to keep cooled air from escaping in summer and cold gusts from entering in the winter.

PREHEATING WATER. To reduce the cost of heating water, wrap 25 ft. of flexible copper tubing around the exhaust flue of your furnace (prevent contact of dissimilar metals by separating them with high-temperature insulating strips). Then hook one end of the tubing to the water source, and run the other end into your water heater. Cover the copper with 1200° F. fiberglass insulation. In this way, water going into the water heater is preheated by the furnace.

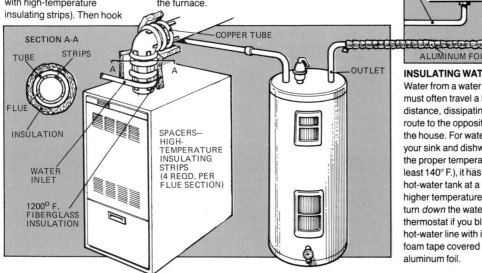

SECTION A-A
TUBE
STRIPS
FLUE
INSULATION
WATER INLET
1200° F. FIBERGLASS INSULATION
A   A
COPPER TUBE
SPACERS— HIGH-TEMPERATURE INSULATING STRIPS (4 REQD. PER FLUE SECTION)
OUTLET
COLD WATER
HOT WATER
ALUMINUM FOIL-COVERED FOAM TAPE

INSULATING WATER LINE.
Water from a water heater must often travel a long distance, dissipating heat en route to the opposite side of the house. For water to reach your sink and dishwasher at the proper temperature (at least 140° F.), it has to leave the hot-water tank at a slightly higher temperature. You can turn *down* the water-heater thermostat if you blanket the hot-water line with inexpensive foam tape covered with aluminum foil.

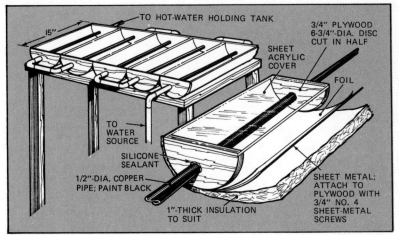

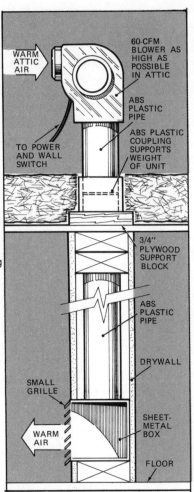

SOLAR WATER HEATER. This solar water-heater trough boils water in 30 minutes when the outside temperature is 70° F. You can combine several troughs, or use a single unit on a camping trip. To build it, cut a 6¾-in.-dia. disc of ¾-in. plywood; cut it in half. Use sheet-metal screws to fasten the wood at both ends of a 15-in.-long piece of sheet metal, cut to proper width. Mark the center of both plywood pieces and bore holes for ½-in.- dia. copper pipe. Glue heavy-duty aluminum foil inside the trough. Insert copper pipe painted black through the two holes, then seal them. Place acrylic cover on trough and glue insulation on back. Hook up one end of the pipe to a water source, the other to a holding tank.

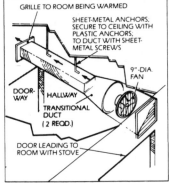

WEATHERSTRIP SAVER. To protect pile weatherstripping on sliding patio doors from wearing out and letting in cold air, lubricate in with silicone spray. First, vacuum all of the grit from the weatherstripping and tracks; then use a silicone spray with a tube applicator (or trade tops with another compatible can with a tube applicator). This will make the door slide more easily as well. File any rough metal edges that may rub against and tear the weatherstripping. Repeat this procedure each summer.

SHARING WARMTH.
Circulating air warmed by a wood stove into adjoining rooms can be a problem. Warm air rises easily, but won't move laterally unless pushed or pulled mechanically. Solve the problem using ductwork and a fan installed at ceiling level. Above the doorway in the warm room, insert a 3¼ x 1¼-in. grille, 1½ in. below the ceiling. On the cold side, use a transitional duct (3¼ x 10¼ in. expanding to 9 in. round) to connect the grille with a 9-in. circular fan drawing 75 c.f.m. Beyond the fan, use another transitional duct to connect the fan with rectangular ductwork. Wire the motor with metal-sheathed cable to a nearby light switch. Suspend the ductwork from right-angle strips of metal screwed into the ceiling joists and ductwork. Finish by painting it the same color as the ceiling.

SPREADING THE HEAT. In a well-insulated home, warmth from the sun cannot penetrate on spring and autumn days, even when the sun is bright. Operating the furnace to take off the chill would be overkill. On these days, the attic (under dark shingles) can stay quite warm. You can capture this heat by installing plastic pipe ducts at each end of the house in a centrally located partition. Top these ducts with 60-c.f.m. blowers in the attic, which feed to small grilles in a sheet-metal box that is pop-riveted together at floor level of the floor below. Each blower is controlled independently by a manual wall switch. When you need heat and the sun's been shining an hour or more, these gadgets do the job, almost for free.

SHOP GUIDE

CUSTOMARY TO METRIC (CONVERSION) Conversion factors can be carried so far they become impractical. In cases below where an entry is exact it is followed by an asterisk (*). Where considerable rounding off has taken place, the entry is followed by a + or a − sign.

Linear Measure

inches	millimeters
1/16	1.5875*
1/8	3.2
3/16	4.8
1/4	6.35*
5/16	7.9
3/8	9.5
7/16	11.1
1/2	12.7*
9/16	14.3
5/8	15.9
11/16	17.5
3/4	19.05*
13/16	20.6
7/8	22.2
15/16	23.8
1	25.4*

inches	centimeters
1	2.54*
2	5.1
3	7.6
4	10.2
5	12.7*
6	15.2
7	17.8
8	20.3
9	22.9
10	25.4*
11	27.9
12	30.5

feet	centimeters	meters
1	30.48*	.3048*
2	61	.61
3	91	.91
4	122	1.22
5	152	1.52
6	183	1.83
7	213	2.13
8	244	2.44
9	274	2.74
10	305	3.05
50	1524*	15.24*
100	3048*	30.48*

1 yard = .9144* meters
1 rod = 5.0292* meters
1 mile = 1.6 kilometers
1 nautical mile = 1.852* kilometers

Weights

ounces	grams
1	28.3
2	56.7
3	85
4	113
5	142
6	170
7	198
8	227
9	255
10	283
11	312
12	340
13	369
14	397
15	425
16	454

Formula (exact):
ounces × 28.349 523 125* = grams

pounds	kilograms
1	.45
2	.9
3	1.4
4	1.8
5	2.3
6	2.7
7	3.2
8	3.6
9	4.1
10	4.5

1 short ton (2000 lbs) = 907 kilograms (kg)
Formula (exact):
pounds × .453 592 37* = kilograms

Fluid Measure

(Milliliters [ml] and cubic centimeters [cc] are equivalent, but it is customary to use milliliters for liquids.)

1 cu in = 16.39 ml
1 fl oz = 29.6 ml
1 cup = 237 ml
1 pint = 473 ml
1 quart = 946 ml
      = .946 liters
1 gallon = 3785 ml
       = 3.785 liters

Formula (exact):
fluid ounces × 29.573 529 562 5*
   = milliliters

Volume

1 cu in = 16.39 cubic centimeters (cc)
1 cu ft = 28 316.7 cc
1 bushel = 35 239.1 cc
1 peck = 8 809.8 cc

Area

1 sq in = 6.45 sq cm
1 sq ft = 929 sq cm
      = .093 sq meters
1 sq yd = .84 sq meters
1 acre = 4 046.9 sq meters
      = .404 7 hectares
1 sq mile = 2 589 988 sq meters
        = 259 hectares
        = 2.589 9 sq kilometers

Miscellaneous

1 British thermal unit (Btu) (mean)
   = 1 055.9 joules
1 horsepower = 745.7 watts
            = .75 kilowatts
caliber (diameter of a firearm's bore in hundredths of an inch)
   = .254 millimeters (mm)

1 atmosphere pressure = 101 325* pascals (newtons per sq meter)
1 pound per square inch (psi) = 6 895 pascals
1 pound per square foot = 47.9 pascals
1 knot = 1.85 kilometers per hour
1 mile per hour = 1.6093 kilometers per hour